Manual of Structural Kinesiology

Manual of Structural Kinesiology

Eleventh edition

Clem W. Thompson
Ph.D., F.A.C.S.M.
Professor of Physical Education, Emeritus
Mankato State University
Mankato, Minnesota

with 152 illustrations

Times Mirror/Mosby College Publishing
St. Louis • Toronto • Boston • Los Altos 1989

Editor: **Pat Coryell**
Editorial Assistant: **Shannon Ruyle**
Designer: **Liz Fett**
Project Manager: **Patricia Gayle May**
Production: **Barbara Merritt**

Eleventh Edition

Copyright © 1989 by Times Mirror/Mosby College Publishing
A division of The C. V. Mosby Company
11830 Westline Industrial Drive, St. Louis, Missouri 63146

Previous editions copyrighted in 1948, 1951, 1956, 1961, 1965, 1969, 1973, 1977, 1981, 1985

Printed in the United States of America

International Standard Book Number: 0-8016-5031-3

C/VH/VH   9   8   7

Preface

It would seem that a book of this type that has gone through ten editions should need little or no changes. Yet the revisions in this edition include a number of improvements that should make both teaching and learning easier.

The *MANUAL OF STRUCTURAL KINESIOLOGY* was first published 40 years ago. It has been revised and updated regularly since then. Its long and continued popularity has been due, in part, to the clear and concise presentation of the material and to the simplicity of its organization. In this edition one joint of the body is considered at a time. An illustration of each muscle of the joint and other interesting facts about each muscle are presented. The muscles are then grouped together as primary movers of each joint.

It has long been my opinion that superficial knowledge of individual muscles or muscle groups is not enough. Provision for in-depth knowledge and understanding of muscles developed by exercise, sports, weight training, and other activities that increase the strength and endurance of all muscle groups must be made.

Audience

Applied kinesiologists, athletic coaches, physical educators, physical therapists, health club instructors, weight training instructors, and others who are responsible for improving and maintaining the muscular strength and endurance of individuals will benefit from this text.

Today it is believed that, rather than developing strength from sports, individuals should develop strength before they participate. The physical fitness revolution of recent decades has resulted in greater emphasis on the development of strength and endurance for all ages. Vigorous exercises, free weights, and modern exercise machines are found in schools, colleges and universities, and health clubs throughout the nation. It is imperative that individuals who know and understand the muscular system be leaders in teaching these activities.

This book can be helpful to those who teach young or old to participate in sports and to those who want to maintain muscular strength and endurance throughout life.

New to this edition

One major change in this edition is the addition of more tear-out worksheets to be used with each chapter. They can be used either for in-class or out-of-class assignments or for testing. Their preliminary use at Mankato State University has proved their helpfulness both for the instructor and student.

A number of other changes include the improvement of student objectives at the beginning of each chapter. The objectives are now more specific and easier to understand.

Chapter organization has also been improved. Two chapters from the previous edition have been combined to form Chapter 4, The Elbow, Radioulnar, Wrist, and Hand Joints.

Chapter 6, The Hip Joint and Pelvic Girdle, and Chapter 8, The Ankle and Foot, have been reorganized. These chapters now include a larger number of muscles. These muscles are listed by joint movements before each individual muscle is presented.

Chapter 5, Muscular Analysis of Upper Extremities, and Chapter 10, Muscular Analysis of Selected Exercises and Activities, have undergone a number of changes. These chapters teach students how to analyze which muscles are used in simple exercises. The exercises to be analyzed have been updated, using examples with modern exercise machines found in schools, colleges and universities, health clubs, and training rooms.

New figures have been included to better illustrate the muscle groups described. It is impossible to prescribe exercises for individual muscles, but a good kinesiology student can prescribe exercises to develop and strengthen the major muscles that produce movement of a joint.

The section on early analysis of exercises, which follows the study of the shoulder area in Chapter 3, has proved to be very successful. Analysis of the muscles and joint action involved in an activity such as chinning helps the student realize that knowledge of the individual and group muscles used in various joint action is essential. Later in the course, when all large muscle groups have been studied, a more detailed analysis of exercises and weight-training activities is included. In addition, reference sources have been included at the end of each chapter for student assignments or reports.

It is my opinion and that of others that this textbook adequately prepares a student in the anatomical consideration standards (joint structure and function and muscular function) established by the Kinesiology Academy.

Acknowledgments

Active, current university instructors of kinesiology were selected by the publisher to review this text. They offered many comments, ideas, and suggestions to improve this edition, for which I am most grateful.

These reviewers are:

Dr. Arnold Goldfuss
East Stroudsberg University
Pennsylvania

Dr. Maurice A. Johnson
Southwest Texas State
University

Dr. Jeffery E. Lander
Auburn University

Dr. Paul Pastor
California State University,
Fullerton

Dr. Thomas Tillman
Oregan State University

Other acknowledgments go to Mr. Ron Carlberg of Carlberg's Creative Photography, Mankato, Minnesota, for the photographs; to Becky Underwood, Stein Anderson, and my son, Bill Thompson, who served as models for the photographs; to my wife, Mary, whose love, patience, and endurance have persisted throughout the years; and to my colleagues at Mankato State University—Dr. Margaret Buck, Dr. Jean McCarthy, and Gordon Graham—for their advice and suggestions as they used the textbook in their classes. My thanks also go to Nancy Roberson, Shannon Ruyle, Susan Clancy, and Barbara Merritt of the Mosby staff who have been most helpful in their assistance and suggestions in preparing the manuscript for publication.

Clem W. Thompson

Contents

Introduction

Kinesiology is defined as the science of human movement. Improvements in muscular strength and physical development through kinesiological principles, coupled with applications of physiology of exercise, have resulted in improved physical performance on all levels.

Within our national association, kinesiology has improved its status. The Council of Kinesiology was founded in 1968, and annual meetings are held at national conventions. Since 1971, a publication entitled *Kinesiological Reviews* has been produced yearly.

A physical revolution that began in the late 1960s and early 1970s is continuing into the 1980s. The wide-scale participation of women in sport competition at all levels, from junior high school to professional sports, is unparalleled in history. In addition, the number of participants in individual sports, generally noncompetitive such as bicycling, jogging, rope skipping, running, walking, and aerobic dancing, has increased tremendously in recent years. It has been estimated that there were approximately 100,000 joggers in the late 1960s, and as we go further into the 1980s, the number has increased to approximately 30 million. Every day of the year someplace in the United States a marathon run is scheduled.

Applied kinesiologists, athletic coaches, physical educators, physical therapists, health club instructors, weight training instructors, and others responsible for the development, maintenance or rehabilitation of the muscular system need to be adequate students of structural kinesiology.

Understanding the physical laws of gravity, leverage, motion, balance, and others is essential. But, as indicated in the preface, this text includes only the most elementary facts in this area. My long and continuous experience as an active instructor of kinesiology has convinced me that it is impossible to adequately teach both of these important aspects in one quarter or in one semester course.

The major revision of this edition is the addition of more tear-out worksheets to be used as each chapter is completed. These worksheets can be used for in-class or out-of-class assignments or for instructor testing. The mastery of the material can be quickly determined by instructors or students.

Throughout the text there runs an undercurrent of the practical understanding of the facts being presented. Interesting facts about individual groups of muscles are presented. Practical laboratory exercises are found at the end of each chapter. The "how and where" technique of muscle palpation is continually emphasized. Consideration of a simple exercise to ensure the development of muscle groups is explored in each chapter. Individual and groups of muscles performing the same function are related to joint movements.

It is difficult for the beginning structural kinesiology student to perform the muscular analysis of various exercises. Chapters 5 and 10 teach these techniques. A competent structural kinesiology student should be able to analyze any exercise or sports activity and indicate the muscle groups being primarily exercised, developed or rehabilitated. Fewer than 100 muscles are described in this text. In my opinion, a thorough knowledge of these muscles is essential for a well-trained structural kinesiology student.

Manual of Structural Kinesiology

Bases for structural kinesiology

Student objectives

• To review the anatomy of the skeletal and muscular systems.

• To describe the various types of joints in the human body.

• To describe and demonstrate the joint movements.

Structural kinesiology is the study of muscles as they are involved in the science of movement. Both skeletal and muscular structures are involved. Bones are different sizes and shapes—particularly at the joints, which allow or limit the movements. Muscles vary greatly in size, shape, and structure from one part of the body to another.

More than 600 muscles are found in the human body. Most people who use this book do not need to know about each individual muscle. A majority of the muscles in the human body are small muscles located in the hands, feet, and spinal column. Coaches, nurses, physical educators, physical therapists, physicians, athletic trainers, and others in health-related fields should have an adequate knowledge and understanding of all the big muscle groups in the body. This is needed to teach others how to strengthen, improve, and maintain these parts of the human body.

Fewer than 100 of the largest and most important muscles, primary movers, are considered in this text. To anatomists and physicians, the knowledge of all muscles is important, but to others, this knowledge is important in that exercises should be provided to strengthen and maintain all of the muscles in the body. In most cases, exercises that involve the larger primary movers also involve the smaller muscles.

Other small muscles in the human body—such as the coracobrachialis, multifidus, plantaris, peroneus tertius, scalenus, serratus posterior, and subclavius—are omitted, since they are exercised with other larger primary movers. In addition, most small muscles of the hand, feet, and spinal column are not considered.

Kinesiology students are frequently unable to see the forest through the trees: they become so engrossed in learning individual muscles that they lose sight of the total muscular system. The "big picture"—that muscle groups move joints in given movements necessary for bodily movement and skilled performance—is missed.

Skeletal and muscular systems

Figure 1-1 is an anterior and posterior view of the skeletal system. Two hundred and six bones make up the skeletal system, which provides support and protection for other systems of the body and provides for attachments of the muscles to the bones by which movement is produced.

FIG. 1-1 • Skeleton, front and back.

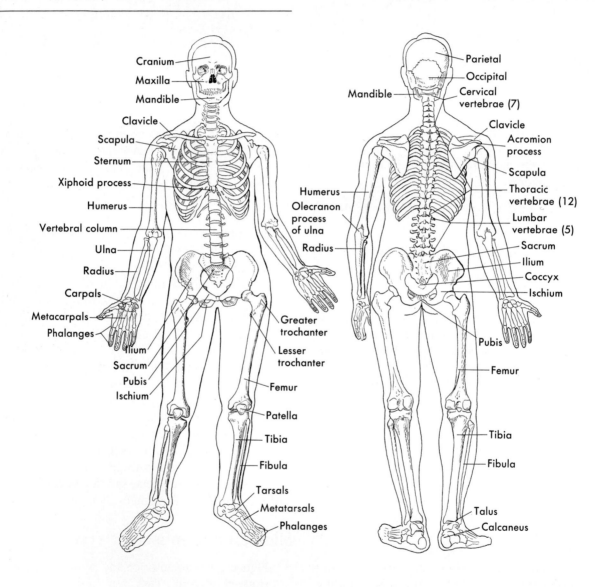

Most students who take this course will have had a course in human anatomy, but a brief review is desirable as you undertake the study of kinesiology. Other chapters will provide additional information and more detailed illustrations of specific bones.

The total superficial muscular system is shown in Figs. 1-2 and 1-3. Any figure is limited, since many muscles are not surface muscles. Still, these figures will help you get a better overview of the entire superficial muscular structure.

Muscles shown in these figures, and many other muscles, will be studied in more detail as each joint of the body is considered in other chapters of the book.

Joints and movements

The articulation of two or more bones allows various types of movements. The extent and type of movement determines the name applied to the joint. The articulations are grouped in three classes, depending on the amount of movement.

Diarthrodial articulations—freely movable joints

Structurally this type of articulation can be divided into six groups:

Arthrodial
A gliding joint with limited movement, as in the bones of the wrist (carpal) and those in the foot (tarsal).

Condyloidal
Type of joint in which the bones permit movement in two planes without accomplishing rotation, as the movement of the radius and ulna on the carpal bones.

Enarthrodial
The ball-and-socket joint, which permits movement in all planes and also rotation in the shoulder and hip joints.

Ginglymus
The hinge joint, which permits a wide range of movement in only one direction in the elbow and knee joints.

Reciprocal reception
The saddle joint, found only in the thumb, that permits ball and socket movement with the exception of rotation.

Trochoidal
The pivot joint, with a rotation movement around a long axis, as the rotation of the radius bone.

Synarthrodial articulations—immovable joints

Found in the cranial bones, ilium, ischium, and pubic articulations.

Amphiarthrodial articulations—slightly movable joints

Found in the spinal column; slight movement is brought about by compression of the disks, vertebrae upon vertebrae.

Bone structure limits the kind and amount of movements in each joint. Some joints have a number of movements, while others are very limited. The type and range of movements are similar in all persons, but the freedom, range, and vigor of movements are limited by ligaments and muscles.

FIG. 1-2 • Muscles of human body, anterior view.

From Chaffee A and Lytle F: Basic physiology and anatomy, ed. 4, Philadelphia, 1980, JB Lippincott Co.

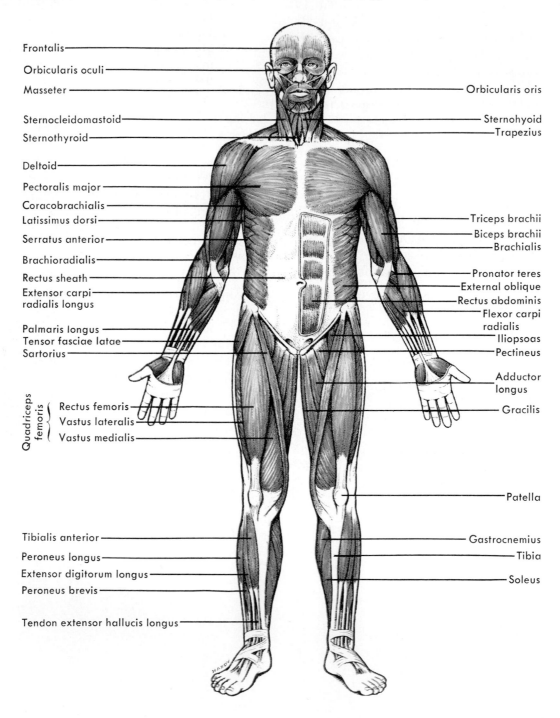

Frontalis

Orbicularis oculi

Masseter

Orbicularis oris

Sternocleidomastoid

Sternohyoid

Sternothyroid

Trapezius

Deltoid

Pectoralis major

Coracobrachialis

Latissimus dorsi

Triceps brachii

Serratus anterior

Biceps brachii

Brachialis

Brachioradialis

Pronator teres

Rectus sheath

External oblique

Extensor carpi
radialis longus

Rectus abdominis

Flexor carpi
radialis

Palmaris longus

Iliopsoas

Tensor fasciae latae

Pectineus

Sartorius

Adductor
longus

Quadriceps femoris { Rectus femoris

Vastus lateralis

Gracilis

Vastus medialis

Patella

Tibialis anterior

Gastrocnemius

Peroneus longus

Tibia

Extensor digitorum longus

Soleus

Peroneus brevis

Tendon extensor hallucis longus

FIG. 1-3 • Muscles of human body, posterior view.

From Chaffee A and Lytle F: Basic physiology and anatomy, ed. 4, Philadelphia, 1980, JB Lippincott Co.

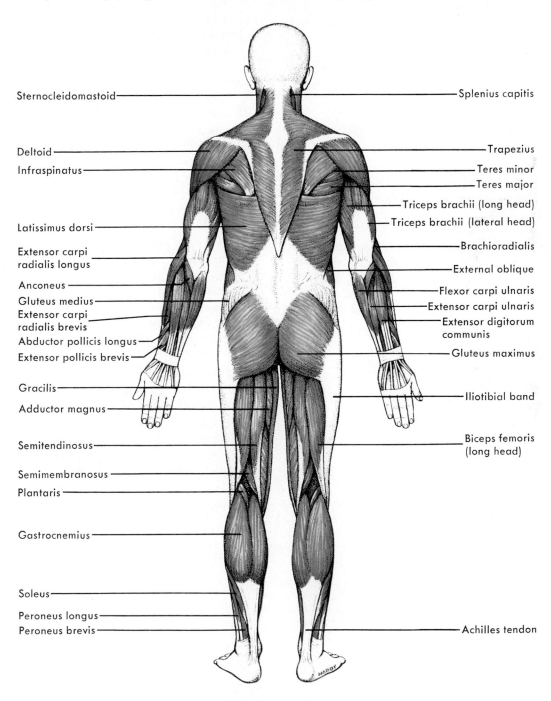

Sternocleidomastoid

Deltoid

Infraspinatus

Latissimus dorsi

Extensor carpi
radialis longus

Anconeus

Gluteus medius

Extensor carpi
radialis brevis

Abductor pollicis longus

Extensor pollicis brevis

Gracilis

Adductor magnus

Semitendinosus

Semimembranosus

Plantaris

Gastrocnemius

Soleus

Peroneus longus

Peroneus brevis

Splenius capitis

Trapezius

Teres minor

Teres major

Triceps brachii (long head)

Triceps brachii (lateral head)

Brachioradialis

External oblique

Flexor carpi ulnaris

Extensor carpi ulnaris

Extensor digitorum
communis

Gluteus maximus

Iliotibial band

Biceps femoris
(long head)

Achilles tendon

Movements in joints

In many joints, several different movements are possible. Some joints permit only flexion and extension; others permit a wide range of movements, depending largely on the joint structure.

Abduction
Movement away from axis of trunk, as in raising arms to the side horizontally, leg sideward, and scapula away from the spinal column.

Adduction
Movement toward axis of trunk, as in lowering arms to the side or leg back to anatomical position.

Flexion
Bending; bringing bones together, as in the elbow joint when the hand is drawn to the shoulder. Bending of the knee in lower extremity. Exception: movement of the humerus to the front from the side is considered flexion of the shoulder joint.

Extension
Straightening; moving bones apart, as when hand moves away from shoulder. Exception: shoulder joint—return movement from shoulder joint flexion.

Eversion
Turning sole outward; weight on inner edge of the foot.

Inversion
Turning sole inward; weight on outer edge of the foot.

Dorsal flexion
Movement of top of foot toward anterior tibia bone.

Plantar flexion
Movement of sole downward toward the floor.

Pronation
Rotation on axis of bone, specifically applied to the forearms, as in turning hand down by rotating radius on the ulna.

Supination
Rotation on axis of bone, specifically applied to forearms, as in turning hand up by rotating the radius on the ulna.

Horizontal flexion (adduction)
Movement of the humerus from the side-horizontal to the front-horizontal position.

Horizontal extension (abduction)
Return to the side-horizontal position.

Rotation inward
Rotation with axis of bone away body, as when the humerus is turned outward.

Rotation outward
Rotation with axis of bone away from body, as when the humerus is turned outward.

Rotation upward
Rotation against gravity, as in turning glenoid fossa upward.

Rotation downward
Rotation with gravity, as in returning glenoid fossa to normal position from upward rotation.

Elevation
Movement upward, as in shrugging the shoulders.

Depression
Movement returning to the normal position.

Circumduction
Circular movement of joint, combining movements; possible in shoulder joint, hip joint, and trunk around a fixing point.

These movements are considered in detail in the chapters to follow as they apply to the individual joints.

Combinations of movements can occur. Flexion or extension can occur with abduction or adduction.

Muscle contraction produces the force that causes joint movement in the human body. It is necessary to understand certain terms as body movement is considered.

The terms most commonly used are *origin* and *insertion*. It can be said that a muscle starts on one bone and ends on another bone. The origin of a muscle is considered the least movable part. The insertion is the most movable part. For example, the brachialis muscle in the arm has its origin (least movable bone) on the humerus and its insertion (most movable bone) on the ulna. In some movements this process can be reversed. The specific joint chapters that follow will explain this phenomenon in more detail. Each muscle studied will have its origin and insertion indicated.

Laboratory and review exercises

As an aid to student learning, and for assignments in-class, out of class, or for teacher testing, tear-out worksheets are found at the end of the text (pages 159-160).

Posterior skeletal worksheet (no. 1)

On the posterior skeletal worksheet, list the names of the bones and all of the prominent features of each bone.

Anterior skeletal worksheet (no. 1)

On the anterior skeletal worksheet list the names of the bones and all of the prominent features of each bone.

Individuals who are involved in teaching others to develop muscular strength, aerobics training, and rehabilitation need adequate knowledge of all the big muscle groups. Students who lack a sound foundation in muscles and muscular actions are at a disadvantage.

Physicians, chiropractors, physical therapists, nurses, and people in some other related health fields need additional study of smaller muscles, nerves, and processes that are beyond the scope of this book.

Additional laboratory and review exercises

1. Observe on a fellow student some of the muscles found in Figs. 1-2 and 1-3.
2. Locate the various types of joints on a human skeleton and a living subject.
3. Individually practice the various joint movements, on yourself or with another subject.

References

Anthony C and Thibodeau G: Textbook of anatomy and physiology, ed 10, 1979, St. Louis, The CV Mosby Co.

Goss CM: Gray's anatomy of the human body, ed. 29, 1973, Philadelphia, Lea and Febiger.

Steindler A: Kinesiology of the human body, 1970, Springfield, Ill, Charles C Thomas, Publisher.

The shoulder girdle 2

Student objectives

• To identify on the skeleton important bone features of the shoulder girdle.

• To label on a skeletal chart the important bone features of the shoulder girdle.

• To draw on a skeletal chart the muscles of the shoulder girdle.

• To draw and indicate on a skeletal chart, using arrows, the movements of the shoulder girdle.

• To demonstrate, using a human subject, all of the movements of the shoulder girdle.

• To palpate the muscles of the shoulder girdle on a human subject.

Brief descriptions of the most important bones in the shoulder region will help you understand the skeletal structure and its relationship to the muscular system.

Bones FIG. 2-1

Two bones are primarily involved in movements of the shoulder girdle. They are the scapula and clavicle, which generally move as a unit.

Movements

Adduction—back toward the spinal column.
Abduction—forward and away from the spinal column.
Rotation upward—turning the glenoid fossa upward and the lower medial border of the scapula away from the spinal column.
Rotation downward—returning the inferior angle of the scapula toward the spinal column and the glenoid fossa to its normal position.
Elevation—as in shrugging the shoulders.
Depression—as in returning to normal position.
   All these movements have their pivotal point at the junction of the clavicle and the sternum.
   Movements of the shoulder girdle can be described as movements of the scapula.

FIG. 2-1 •Right scapula, posterior view.

From Anthony CP and Kolthoff NJ: Textbook of anatomy and
physiology, ed. 9, St. Louis, The CV Mosby Co.

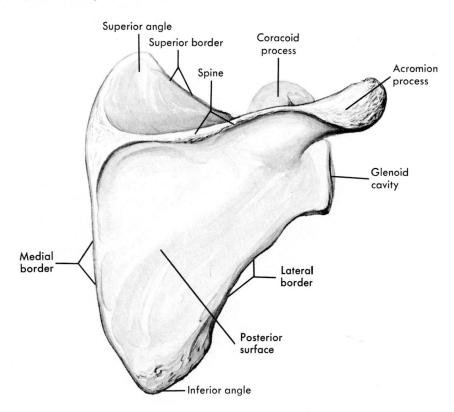

Trapezius muscle FIG. 2-2

Origin

Part I—base of skull, occipital protuberance.

Part II—ligaments of neck.

Part III—spines of seventh cervical and upper three thoracic vertebrae.

Part IV—spines of fourth through twelfth thoracic verebrae.

Insertion

Part I—posterior aspect of the outer third of the clavicle.

Part II—border of the acromion process.

Part III—upper border of the scapular spine.

Part IV—triangular space at the base of the spine.

Actions

Part I—elevation of the scapula.

Part II—elevation, upward rotation, and adduction of the scapula.

Park III—adduction of the scapula.

Part IV—depression, adduction, and upward rotation of the scapula.

Palpation

Large area up and down from the neck region to the twelfth thoracic spine and laterally from the vertebral column to the scapula.

Observation and exercise

Part I is a thin and relatively weak part of the muscle. It provides some elevation of the clavicle. As a mover of the head it is of minor importance.

Part II is a stronger, thicker muscle and provides a stronger elevation, upward rotation, and adduction movement of the scapula.

Part III is a primary mover in adduction of the scapula.

Part IV assists in adduction and rotates the scapula upward.

When all the parts of the trapezius are working together, they tend to pull upward and adduct at the same time. Typical action of the trapezius muscle is fixation of the scapula for deltoideus action. Continuous action in upward rotation of the scapula permits the arms to be raised overhead. The muscle is always used in preventing the glenoid fossae from being pulled down during the lifting of objects with the arms. It is also seen typically in action during the holding of an object overhead. Holding the arm at the side horizontally shows typical fixation of the scapula by the trapezius muscle, while the deltoideus muscle holds the arm in that position. The muscle is used strenuously when lifting with the hands, as in picking up a heavy wheelbarrow. The trapezius must prevent the scapula from being pulled downward. Carrying objects on the tip of the shoulder also calls this muscle into play. Other good exercises are shoulder shrugs and bent rowing with a barbell.

FIG. 2-2 • Trapezius muscle, O, origin; I, insertion.

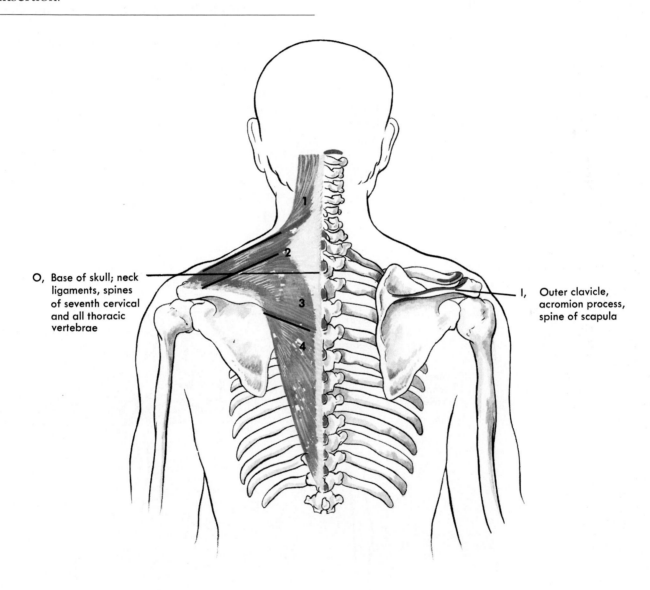

O, Base of skull; neck ligaments, spines of seventh cervical and all thoracic vertebrae

I, Outer clavicle, acromion process, spine of scapula

Levator scapulae muscle FIG. 2-3

Origin

Transverse processes of the upper four cervical vertebrae.

Insertion

Medial border of the scapula above the base of the scapular spine.

Action

Elevates the medial margin of the scapula.

Palpation

Cannot be palpated; under the trapezius muscle.

Observation and exercise

Shrugging the shoulders calls the levator scapulae muscle into play along with the trapezius muscle. Fixation of the scapula by the pectoralis minor muscle allows the levator scapulae muscles on both sides to extend the neck or to flex laterally if used on one side only.

Rhomboideus muscles—major and minor FIG. 2-4

Origin

Spinous processes of the last cervical and the first five thoracic vertebrae.

Insertion

Medial border of the scapula, below the spine.

Action

The rhomboideus major and minor muscles work together.

Adduction—draw the scapula toward the spinal column; elevate slightly as they adduct.

Rotation downward—from the upward rotated position; they draw the scapula in a downward rotation.

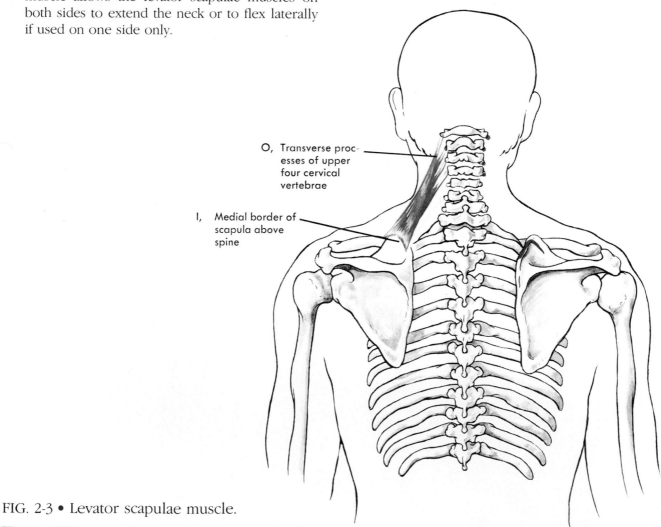

O, Transverse processes of upper four cervical vertebrae

I, Medial border of scapula above spine

FIG. 2-3 • Levator scapulae muscle.

Palpation

Cannot be palpated; under the trapezius muscle.

Observation and exercise

The rhomboideus muscles fix the scapula in adduction when the muscles of the shoulder joint adduct or extend the arm. These muscles are used powerfully in chinning. As one hangs from the horizontal bar, suspended by the hands, the scapula tends to be pulled away from the top of the chest. When the chinning movement begins, it is the rhomboideus muscles that draw the medial border of the scapula down and back toward the spinal column. Note their favorable position to do this.

The trapezius and rhomboideus muscles, working together, produce adduction with some slight elevation of the scapula. To prevent this elevation, the latissimus dorsi muscle is called into play.

Chins and dips are excellent exercises for developing this muscle.

FIG. 2-4 • Rhomboideus muscles (major and minor).

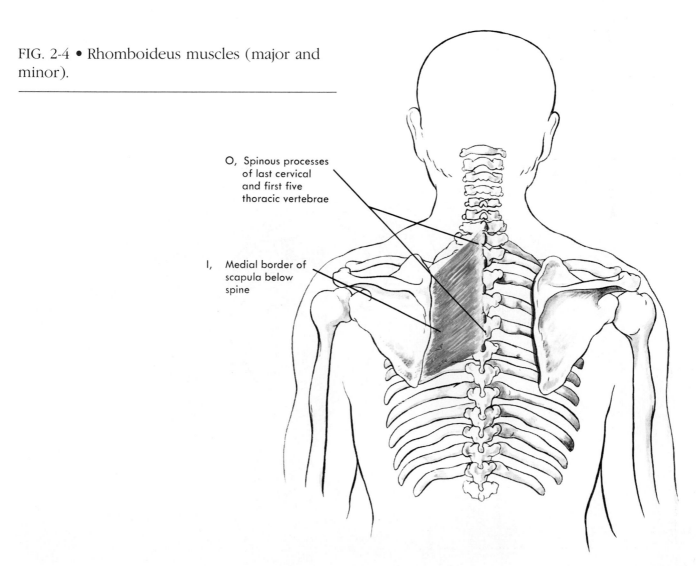

O, Spinous processes of last cervical and first five thoracic vertebrae

I, Medial border of scapula below spine

Serratus anterior muscle FIG. 2-5

Origin

Surface of the upper nine ribs at the side of the chest.

Insertion

Costal aspect of the whole length of the medial border of the scapula.

Action

Abduction—draws the medial border of the scapula away from the vertebrae.

Rotation upward—longer lower fibers tend to draw the inferior angle of the scapula farther away from the vertebrae, thus rotating the scapula upward slightly.

Palpation

Front and lateral side of the chest below the fifth and sixth ribs.

Observation and exercise

The serratus anterior muscle is used commonly in movements drawing the scapula forward with slight upward rotation, such as throwing a baseball, shooting and guarding in basketball, and tackling in football. It works along with the pectoralis major muscle in typical action, such as throwing a baseball.

The serratus anterior muscle is used strongly in doing push-ups and especially in the last 5 to 10 degrees of motion. The bench press and overhead press are good exercises for this muscle. A winged scapula condition indicates a definite muscular weakness.

FIG. 2-5 • Serratus anterior muscle.

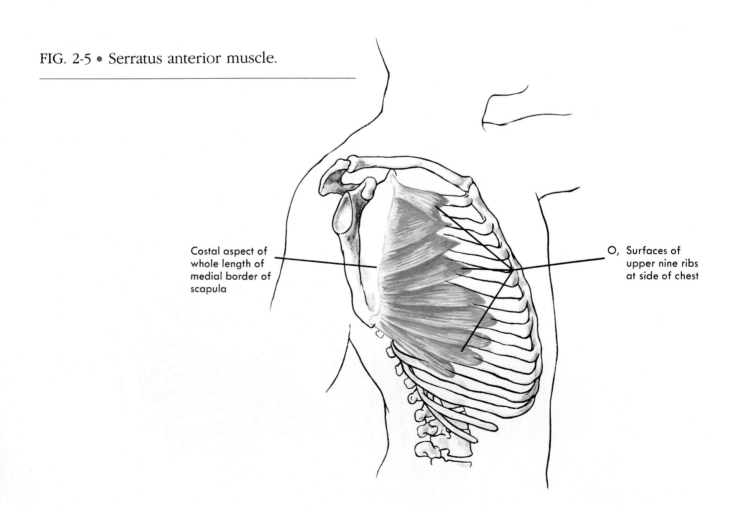

Costal aspect of whole length of medial border of scapula

O, Surfaces of upper nine ribs at side of chest

Pectoralis minor muscle FIG. 2-6

Origin

Outer surfaces of the third to fifth ribs.

Insertion

Coracoid process of the scapula.

Action

Abduction—draws the scapula forward and tends to tilt the lower border away from the ribs.

Downward rotation—as it abducts, it draws the scapula downward; when the scapula is rotated upward, it will help depress it.

Palpation

Difficult to palpate but can be palpated under the pectoralis major muscle in the pit of the shoulder during powerful downward movement.

Observation and exercise

The pectoralis minor muscle is used, along with the serratus anterior muscle, in true abduction (no rotation). This is seen particularly in movements such as push-ups. True abduction of the scapula is necessary. Therefore the serratus anterior draws the scapula forward with a tendency toward upward rotation, the pectoralis minor pulls forward with a tendency toward downward rotation, and the two pulling together give true abduction, which is necessary in push-ups. These muscles will be seen working together in most movements of pushing with the hands.

FIG. 2-6 • Pectoralis minor muscle.

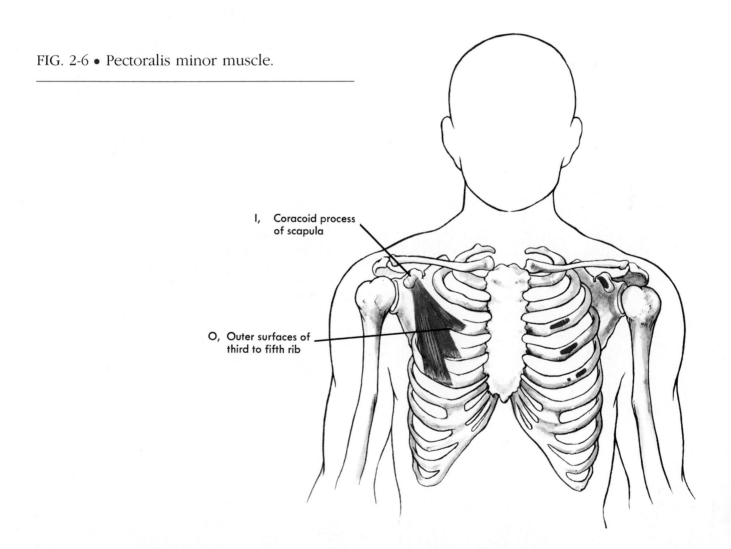

I, Coracoid process of scapula

O, Outer surfaces of third to fifth rib

Laboratory and review exercises

As an aid to student learning and for assignments, in-class, out-of-class or for teacher testing, tear-out worksheets are found at the end of the text (pages 161-162).

Skeletal worksheet (no. 1)

Draw and label on the worksheet the following listed muscles:
(a) Trapezius
(b) Rhomboideus major and minor
(c) Serratus anterior
(d) Levator scapulae

Human figure worksheet (no. 2)

Label and indicate by arrows the following movements of the shoulder girdle:
(a) Adduction
(b) Abduction
(c) Rotation upward
(d) Rotation downward
(e) Elevation
(f) Depression

Additional laboratory and review exercises

1. Locate the following prominent skeletal features on a human skeleton and on a subject:
   a. *Scapula*
      (1) Medial border
      (2) Inferior angle
      (3) Superior angle
      (4) Coracoid process
      (5) Spine of scapula
      (6) Glenoid cavity
      (7) Acromion process
      (8) Supraspinatus fossa
      (9) Infraspinatus fossa
   b. *Clavicle*
      (1) Sternal end
      (2) Acromial end
2 How and where do you palpate the following muscles on a human subject?
   a. Serratus anterior
   b. Trapezius
   c. Rhomboideus major and minor
   d. Levator scapulae
   e. Pectoralis minor
   NOTE: *How* means resisting a primary movement of the muscle. Some muscles have several primary movements, such as the trapezius rotation upward and adduction. *Where* refers to the location on the body where the muscle can be felt.
3. Demonstrate the following shoulder girdle movements:
   a. Adduction
   b. Abduction
   c. Rotation upward
   d. Rotation downward
   e. Elevation
   f. Depression
4. List the muscles that are primarily responsible for the following actions:
   a. Shoulder girdle adduction
   b. Shoulder girdle abduction
   c. Shoulder girdle elevation
   d. Shoulder girdle depression

The shoulder joint 3

Student objectives

• To identify on a human skeleton or human subject the most important bone structures of the shoulder joint.

• To label on a skeletal chart the important bone structures of the shoulder joint.

• To draw and label on a skeletal chart the muscles of the shoulder joint.

• To demonstrate with a fellow student all of the movements of the shoulder joint.

• To label a human skeletal chart with arrows to indicate the movements of the shoulder joint.

• To organize and list the muscles that produce the primary movements of the shoulder girdle and shoulder joint.

The only attachment of the shoulder joint to the axial skeleton is with the clavicle. Movements of the shoulder joint are many and varied. The loose union of the humerus and scapula (about an inch) with the ball and socket joint are the main factors. It is unusual to have movement of the humerus without scapula movement. When the humerus is flexed and abducted, the scapula is elevated and abducted. Adduction and extension of the humerus results in depression and adduction of the scapula.

Observation

The structural nature of the shoulder joint, a ball-and-socket joint, makes possible a wide variety of movements and combinations of movements. Movement of the humerus from the side position is common in throwing, tackling, and striking activities. Flexion and extension of the shoulder joint are performed frequently when supporting the body weight in a hanging position or in a movement from a prone position on the ground. Shoulder joint muscles can be easily distinguished from shoulder girdle muscles, since the shoulder joint muscles are attached to the humerus, or radioulnar bones.

The shoulder joint is a frequently injured part of the body, because the ligamenteous structure is not strong enough to maintain adequate protection for the joint. The generally weak muscular strength of this joint is another important factor in injuries.

A frequent injury is to the rotator cuff. The supraspinatus, infraspinatus, teres minor, and subscapularis muscles make up the rotator cuff. They are small muscles that attach to the front, rear, and top of the head of the humerus. Due to their insertions they are able to rotate the humerus, an essential movement in this freely movable joint.

Bones FIGS. 2-1 and 3-1

The scapula, clavicle, and humerus serve as attachments for most of the muscles of the shoulder joint.

Movements

Abduction—horizontal upward movement of the humerus to the side.

Adduction—return from abduction.

Flexion—movement of the humerus to the front, a forward upward movement.

Extension—return from flexion.

Horizontal adduction (flexion)—movement of the humerus from the side-horizontal to the front-horizontal position.

Horizontal abduction (extension)—return to the side-horizontal position.

Outward rotation—movement of the humerus around its long axis to the lateral side.

Inward rotation—return to the original position.

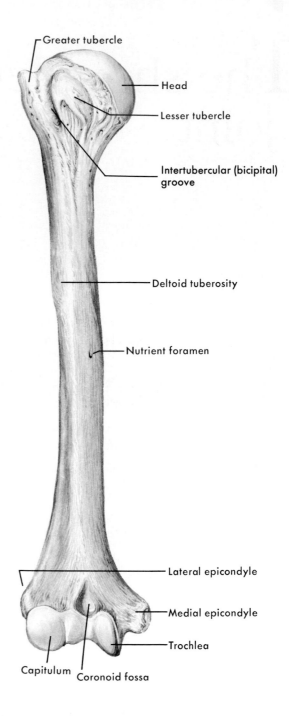

FIG. 3-1 • Right humerus, anterior view.

From Anthony CP and Kolthoff NJ: Textbook of anatomy and physiology, ed. 9, St. Louis, The CV Mosby Co.

Deltoideus muscle FIG. 3-2

Origin

Front outer third of the clavicle, border of the acromion, and lower edge of the spine of the scapula.

Insertion

Deltoideus tubercle on the middle outer surface of the humerus.

Action

True abduction—entire muscle.
Flexion and inward rotation—anterior fibers.
Horizontal adduction (flexion) and inward rotation—anterior fibers.
Extension and outward rotation—posterior fibers.
Horizontal abduction (extension) and outward rotation—posterior fibers.

Palpation

Over the head of the humerus from the anterior to the posterior side.

Observation and exercise

The deltoideus muscle is used commonly in any lifting movement. The trapezius muscle fixes the scapula as the deltoideus pulls on the humerus. The anterior interior fibers of the deltoideus muscle flex and rotate the humerus inward. The posterior fibers extend and rotate the humerus outward. The anterior fibers also horizontally flex (adduction) and rotate the humerus inward, and the posterior fibers horizontally extend (abduction) and rotate the humerus outward.

This muscle is used in all lifting movements if the arms are at the side in lifting.

Any movement of the humerus on the scapula will involve part or all of the deltoideus muscle.

Lifting the humerus from the side to the position of abduction at the side horizontally is a typical action of the deltoideus. Placing a dumbbell in the hand and raising the arm directly to the side is an excellent exercise for this muscle.

FIG. 3-2 • Deltoideus muscle.

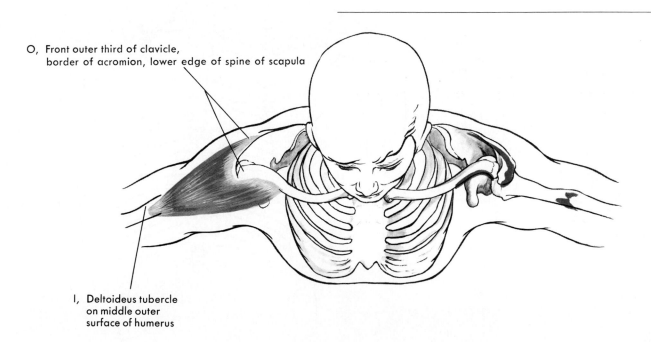

O, Front outer third of clavicle, border of acromion, lower edge of spine of scapula

I, Deltoideus tubercle on middle outer surface of humerus

Supraspinatus muscle FIG. 3-3

Origin
Supraspinous fossa.

Insertion
Top of the greater tubercle of the humerus.

Action
Weak abduction.

Palpation
Cannot be palpated; under the deltoideus muscle.

Observation and exercise

The supraspinatus muscle holds the head of the humerus in the glenoid fossa. This muscle is developed with the deltoideus muscle in true abduction. It is important in throwing movements, since in the follow-through it is the supraspinatus that holds the head of the humerus in the glenoid fossa without interfering with the movement. It is a rotator cuff muscle which can be overused or injured.

The supraspinatus muscle may be called into play whenever the middle fibers of the deltoideus muscle are used. It is exercised in the same movement described in total deltoideus action.

FIG. 3-3 • Supraspinatus muscle.

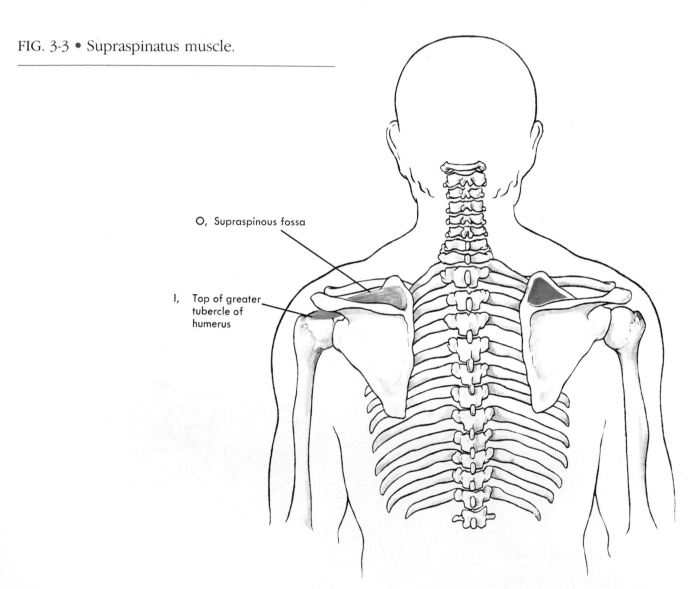

O, Supraspinous fossa

I, Top of greater tubercle of humerus

Infraspinatus and teres minor muscles FIG. 3-4

Origin

Posterior surface of the scapula below the spine and lateral border.

Insertion

Greater tubercle of the humerus on the posterior side.

Action

Horizontal abduction (extension)—draws the humerus from the front horizontal position to the side horizontal position.

Extension—draws the humerus from the front horizontal position down to the side position; rotates outward as it extends.

Outward rotation—rotation to the outside.

Palpation

Between the scapula and the humerus on the posterior side just below the posterior fibers of the deltoideus muscle.

Observation and exercise

The infraspinatus and teres minor muscles are effective when the rhomboideus muscles fix the scapula. When the humerus is rotated outward, the rhomboideus muscles flatten the scapula to the back and fix the scapula so that the humerus may be rotated.

The deep muscles under the deltoideus are known as the "rotator cuff" muscles (see p. 26). They are the infraspinatus, teres minor, supraspinatus, and subscapularis muscles. The tendons of these muscles are interwoven into the joint capsule. They help hold the head of the humerus in the glenoid cavity in addition to rotating the bone. Injuries to this muscle group are frequent in basketball, baseball, football, and other sports that involve strenuous shoulder joint actions. These two muscles (the infraspinatus and the teres minor) are part of the group.

Exercises in which the arms are pulled down bring the infraspinatus and teres major, and latissimus dorsi into powerful contraction. Chinning, rope climbing, and dips on parallel bars are good exercises for these muscles.

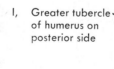

I, Greater tubercle of humerus on posterior side

O, Posterior surface of scapula below spine and lateral border

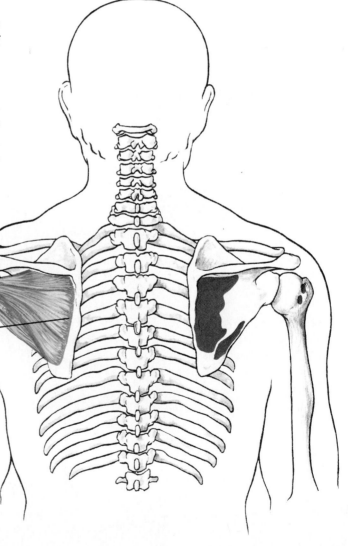

FIG. 3-4 • Infraspinatus and teres minor muscles.

Subscapularis muscle FIG. 3-5

Origin

Entire anterior surface of the subscapular fossa.

Insertion

Lesser tubercle of the humerus.

Action

Extension—draws the humerus from the front horizontal position down to the side.

Rotation inward—rotates the humerus inward as it depresses.

Adduction—draws the arm down to the side from the side horizontal position and rotates inward as it adducts.

Palpation

Cannot be palpated.

Observation and exercise

The subscapularis muscle, another rotator cuff muscle, holds the head of the humerus in the glenoid fossa from below. It acts with the latissimus dorsi and teres major muscles in its typical movement but is less powerful in its action because of its proximity to the joint. The muscle also requires the help of the rhomboideus in fixing the scapula to make it effective in the described movements. See page 26 for additional exercises.

Muscle identification

In Figs. 3-6 and 3-7, identify the anterior and posterior muscles of the shoulder joint and shoulder girdle. Compare Figs. 3-6 and 3-7 with Fig. 3-8.

FIG. 3-5 • Subscapularis muscle.

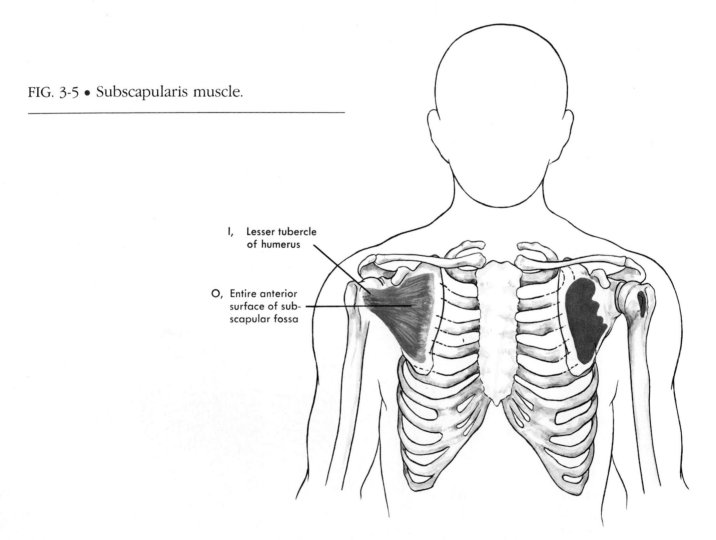

I, Lesser tubercle of humerus

O, Entire anterior surface of sub-scapular fossa

FIG. 3-6 • Posterior shoulder joint and shoulder girdle muscles.

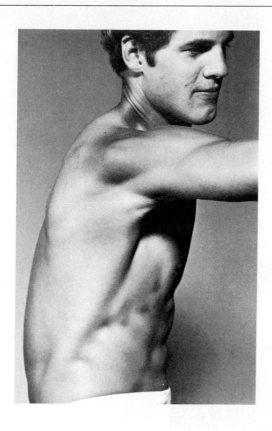

FIG. 3-7 • Anterior shoulder joint and shoulder girdle muscles.

FIG. 3-8 • Posterior muscles.

Modified from Anthony CP and Kolthoff NJ: Textbook of anatomy and physiology, ed. 9, St. Louis, The CV Mosby Co.

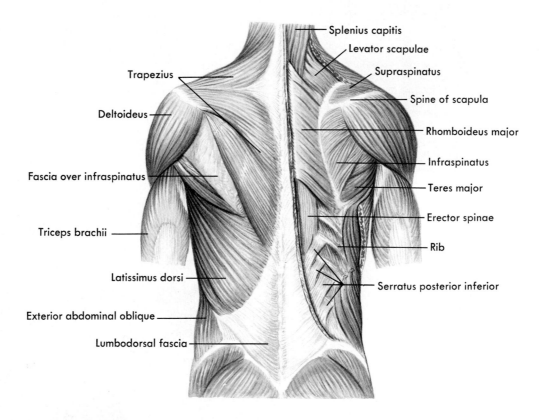

Splenius capitis

Levator scapulae

Trapezius

Supraspinatus

Deltoideus

Spine of scapula

Rhomboideus major

Fascia over infraspinatus

Infraspinatus

Teres major

Triceps brachii

Erector spinae

Rib

Latissimus dorsi

Serratus posterior inferior

Exterior abdominal oblique

Lumbodorsal fascia

Teres major muscle FIG. 3-9

Origin

Lower third of the lateral border of the scapula.

Insertion

Inner lip of the intertubercular groove of the humerus.

Action

Extension—draws the arm from the front-horizontal position down to the side.

Inward rotation—as it adducts, it rotates the humerus inward.

Adduction—draws the arm from the side-horizontal position down to the side and rotates inward as it adducts.

Palpation

Posterior surface, diagonally upward from the inferior angle of the scapula.

Observation and exercise

The teres major muscle is effective only when the rhomboideus muscles fix the scapula or move the scapula in a downward rotation. Otherwise the scapula would move forward to meet the arm.

This muscle works effectively with the latissimus dorsi. It is said to be latissimus dorsi's "little helper." See page 26 for other exercises.

FIG. 3-9 • Teres major muscle.

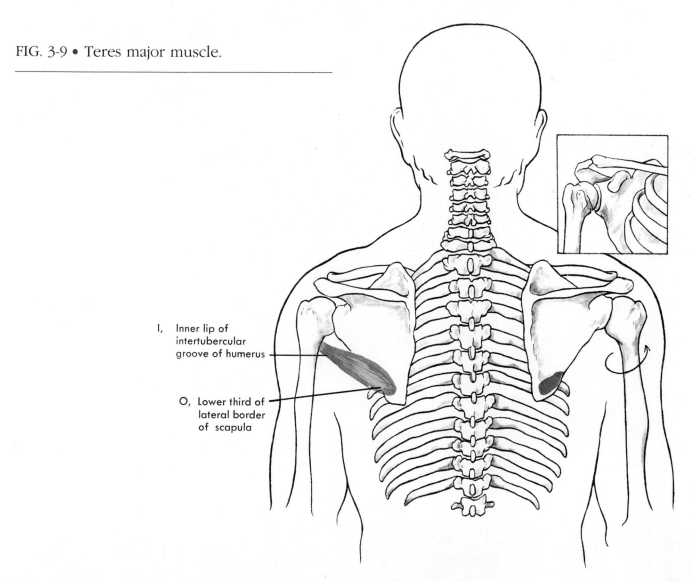

I, Inner lip of intertubercular groove of humerus

O, Lower third of lateral border of scapula

Latissimus dorsi muscle FIG. 3-10

Origin

Posterior crest of the ilium, back of the sacrum and spinous processes of the lumbar and lower six thoracic vertebrae, and slips from the lower three ribs.

Insertion

Medial side of the intertubercular groove of the humerus.

Action

Extension—draws the arm from a front-horizontal position down to the side position.

Rotation inward—as it draws the arm down in depression, it rotates inward with a strong pull.

Horizontal abduction (extension)—draws the arm from the front to the side-horizontal position.

Adduction—draws the arm to the side from the side-horizontal position and again rotates inward as it adducts.

Palpation

Lateral, posterior aspect of the trunk below the armpit.

Observation and exercise

The latissimus dorsi muscle has strong action in downward rotation and adduction of the humerus. It is one of the most important extensor muscles of the humerus and contracts powerfully in chinning.

Exercises in which the arms are pulled down bring the latissimus dorsi muscle into powerful contraction. Chinning, rope climbing, dips on parallel bars, and other uprise movements on the horizontal bar are good examples. In barbell exercises the basic rowing and pullover exercises are good for developing the "lats."

FIG. 3-10 • Latissimus dorsi muscle.

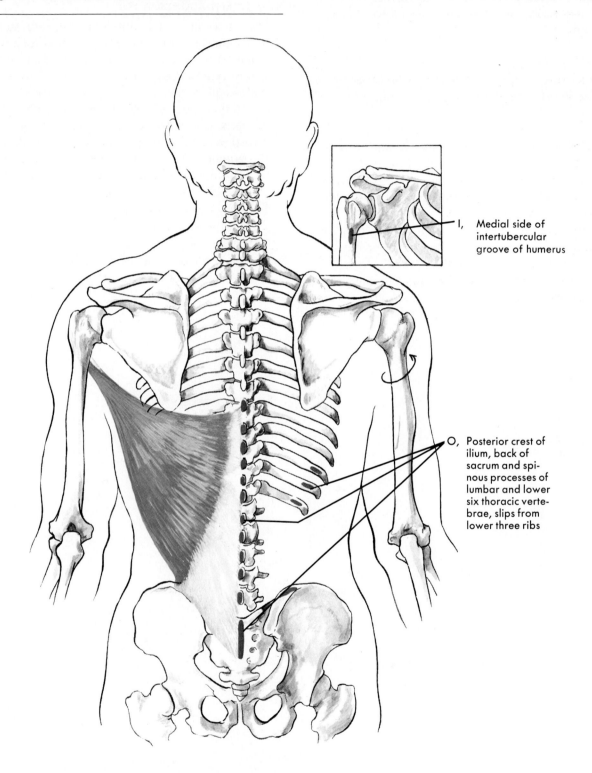

I, Medial side of intertubercular groove of humerus

O, Posterior crest of ilium, back of sacrum and spinous processes of lumbar and lower six thoracic vertebrae, slips from lower three ribs

Pectoralis major muscle FIG. 3-11

Origin

Inner half of the anterior surface of the clavicle, anterior surface of the costal cartilages of the first six ribs, and adjoining portion of the sternum.

Insertion

Flat tendon 2 or 3 inches wide to the outer lip of the intertubercular groove of the humerus.

Action

Flexion—draws the arm forward and upward from the side.

Extension—extends the humerus, particularly when it has been moved above the shoulder level.

Horizontal adduction (flexion)—draws the arm powerfully from the side-horizontal position to the front-horizontal position.

Rotation inward—rotates the humerus inward as it flexes; with the arm at the side, the muscle will draw the arm forward, upward, and across the chest and rotate inward.

Adduction-abduction—depends on the position of the humerus.

Palpation

Broad area of the chest region between the clavicle and the sixth rib.

Observation and exercise

The pectoralis major muscle aids the serratus anterior muscle in drawing the scapula forward as it moves the humerus in flexion and inward rotation. Typical action is shown in throwing a baseball. As the humerus is flexed, it is rotated inward and the scapula is drawn forward with upward rotation. It also works as a helper of the latissimus dorsi muscle when extending and adducting the humerus from a raised position.

The pectoralis major and the anterior deltoideus work closely together. The pectoralis major is used powerfully in push-ups, pull-ups, throwing, and serving in tennis. With a barbell, the subject takes a supine position on a bench with the arm at the side and moves the arm to a front-horizontal position.

FIG. 3-11 • Pectoralis major muscle.

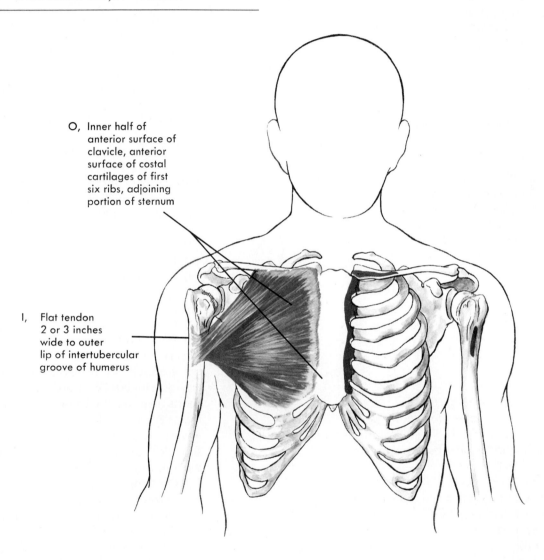

O, Inner half of anterior surface of clavicle, anterior surface of costal cartilages of first six ribs, adjoining portion of sternum

I, Flat tendon 2 or 3 inches wide to outer lip of intertubercular groove of humerus

29

Laboratory and review exercises

As an aid to student learning and for assignments, in-class, out-of-class, or for teacher testing, tear-out worksheets are found at the end of the text (pages 163-164).

Skeletal worksheet (no. 1)

Draw and label on the worksheet the following muscles:
(a) Deltoideus
(b) Supraspinatus
(c) Subscapularis
(d) Teres major
(e) Infraspinatus and teres minor
(f) Latissimus dorsi
(g) Pectoralis major

Additional laboratory and review exercises

1. Locate the following parts of the humerus on a human skeleton and on a subject:
   a. Skeleton
      (1) Greater tubercle
      (2) Lesser tubercle
      (3) Neck
      (4) Shaft
      (5) Intertubercular groove
      (6) Medial epicondyle
      (7) Lateral epicondyle
      (8) Trochlea
      (9) Capitulum
   b. Subject
      (1) Shaft
      (2) Medial epicondyle
      (3) Lateral epicondyle
2. How and where do you palpate the following muscles on a human subject?
   (a) Deltoideus
   (b) Teres major
   (c) Infraspinatus and teres minor
   (d) Latissimus dorsi
   (e) Pectoralis major
   NOTE: Using the pectoralis major muscle, indicate how various actions allow muscle palpation.

Human figure worksheet (no. 2)

Label and indicate by arrows the following listed movements of the shoulder joint:
(a) Abduction
(b) Adduction
(c) Flexion
(d) Extension
(e) Horizontal flexion (adduction)
(f) Horizontal extension (extension)

3. Demonstrate and locate on a human subject the muscles that are primarily used in the following shoulder joint movements:
   (a) Abduction
   (b) Adduction
   (c) Flexion
   (d) Extension
   (e) Horizontal adduction
   (f) Horizontal abduction
   (g) Outward rotation
   (h) Inward rotation
4. Why is it essential that both anterior and posterior muscles of the shoulder joint be properly developed? What are some activities or sports that would cause unequal development? Equal development?
5. Analyze movements and muscles in both shoulder girdle and shoulder joints when the following activities are performed:
   (a) Chinning (actual pull)
   (b) Throwing a baseball (throw only)
   (c) Batting a baseball (striking ball)
   (d) Standing on hands
6. Fill in the movements and muscle actions of the shoulder girdle and shoulder joint on the chart on p. 31. List the muscles primarily responsible for each movement.

Muscle analysis chart • Shoulder girdle and shoulder joint

Shoulder girdle	Shoulder joint
Adduction	Extension
Abduction	Flexion
Elevation	Horizontal adduction
Depression	Horizontal abduction
	Outward rotation
	Inward rotation
	Adduction
	Abduction

References

Garth WP, et al: Occult anterior subluxations of the shoulder in noncontact sports, Am J Sports Medicine 15:579, November-December 1987.

Stacey E: Pitching injuries to the shoulder, Athletic Journal 65:44, January 1984.

The elbow, radioulnar, wrist, and hand joints

4

. . . .

Student objectives

• To identify on a human skeleton the most important bone features of the elbow, wrist, and hand.

• To label the important bone features on a skeletal chart.

• To draw and label the muscles on a skeletal chart.

• To palpate the muscles on a human subject.

• To organize and list the muscles that produce the primary movements of the elbow joint, wrist, and hand.

Anatomically there is a clear distinction between these joints. Functionally the distinction is more difficult to make. Even the simplest movement—for example, eating—involves all of the joints and requires considerable coordination.

Sport skills and other exercise activities require the use of all of these joints: flexion or extension of the elbow joint, pronation or supination of the radioulnar joint, flexion or extension and abduction and adduction of the wrist and hand.

A large number of muscles are used in these movements. In each wrist and hand there are 30 muscles, of which 15 are intrinsic (inside) muscles.

For most students who use this text, an extensive knowledge of these muscles is not necessary. Athletic trainers, physical therapists, occupational therapists, chiropractors, anatomists, physicians, and nurses require a more extensive knowledge. References at the end of this chapter will provide additional sources from which this information can be secured.

The larger, more important muscles of each joint will be included, providing a limited knowledge of this area. The prescription of exercises to provide normal strength and development of this area is not difficult. It can be said that fingertip push-ups will exercise most of these muscles.

THE ELBOW JOINT
Bones FIG. 4-1

The ulna bone articulates with the humerus in a manner that allows for only the movements of flexion and extension. The pronation and supination movements are possible as a result of the different type of articulation of the radius and humerus. In this section only the elbow joint is considered.

Movements

Flexion—movement of the forearm to the shoulder by bending the elbow.

Extension—return to straight arm.

Pronation—movement of the radius on the ulna by moving the hand from the palm-up to the palm-down position.

Supination—movement of the radius on the ulna by moving the hand from the palm-down to the palm-up position.

FIG. 4-1 • Elbow joint.

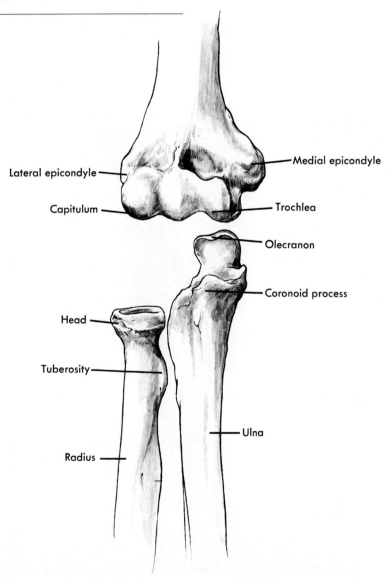

Lateral epicondyle

Capitulum

Medial epicondyle

Trochlea

Olecranon

Coronoid process

Head

Tuberosity

Ulna

Radius

Biceps brachii muscle FIG. 4-2

Origin

Two heads—top of the coracoid process and upper lip of the glenoid fossa.

Insertion

Tuberosity of the radius.

Action

Flexion of the elbow.
Supination of the forearm.
Weak flexion of the shoulder joint.

Palpation

Easily palpated on the anterior aspect of the humerus.

FIG. 4-2 • Biceps brachii muscle.

Observation and exercise

The biceps is a two-joint muscle—shoulder and elbow joints. Some authorities consider it to be a three-joint muscle—shoulder, elbow, and radial-ulnar. It is weak in any actions at the shoulder joint and is the most powerful flexor of the elbow joint. With the elbow joint in a supinated position (palms toward the face), it is most powerful and both flexes and supinates the joint. Palms away from the face (pronation) decreases the effectiveness of the biceps, partly as a result of the disadvantageous pull of the muscle as the radius rotates. The same muscles are used in elbow joint flexion, whether it is pronated or supinated.

Flexion of the forearm, known as "curling," with a barbell in the hands is an excellent exercise to develop the biceps brachii. This movement can be performed one arm at a time with dumbbells or both arms simultaneously with a barbell. Other activities in which there is powerful flexion of the forearm are chinning and rope climbing.

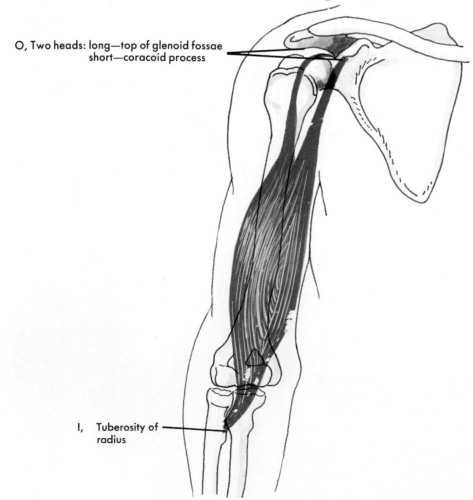

O, Two heads: long—top of glenoid fossae
short—coracoid process

I, Tuberosity of radius

Brachialis muscle FIG. 4-3

Origin

Lower half of the anterior portion of the humerus.

Insertion

Coronoid process of the ulna.

Action

True flexion of the elbow.

Palpation

Lateral side of the upper arm under the biceps brachii muscle.

Observation and exercise

The brachialis muscle is used along with other flexor muscles, whether in pronation or supination. It pulls on the ulna, which does not rotate, thus making this muscle the only pure flexor of this joint.

The brachialis muscle is called into action whenever the elbow flexes. It is exercised along with each of the exercises described for the biceps brachii, pronator teres, and brachioradialis muscles.

FIG. 4-3 • Brachialis muscle.

Modified from Anthony CP and Kolthoff NJ: Textbook of anatomy and physiology, ed. 9, St. Louis, The CV Mosby Co.

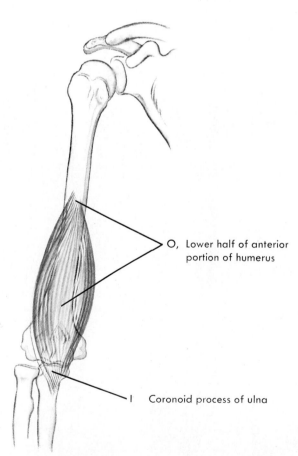

O, Lower half of anterior portion of humerus

I Coronoid process of ulna

Brachioradialis muscle FIG. 4-4

Origin

Lower two thirds of the outer condyloid ridge of the humerus.

Insertion

Outer surface of the lower end of the radius at the styloid process.

Action

Flexion of the elbow.
Pronation from supinated position.
Supination from pronated position.

Palpation

On the lateral anterior side of the forearm.

Observation and exercise

The brachioradialis muscle acts in a midposition between pronation and supination. In a supinated position of the forearm, it tends to pronate as it flexes. In a pronated position, it tends to supinate as it flexes. This muscle is favored in its action of flexion when the midposition between pronation and supination is assumed, as previously suggested. Its insertion at the end of the radius makes it a strong elbow flexor.

For activities and exercises requiring flexion of the elbow, see p. 34.

FIG. 4-4 • Brachioradialis muscle.

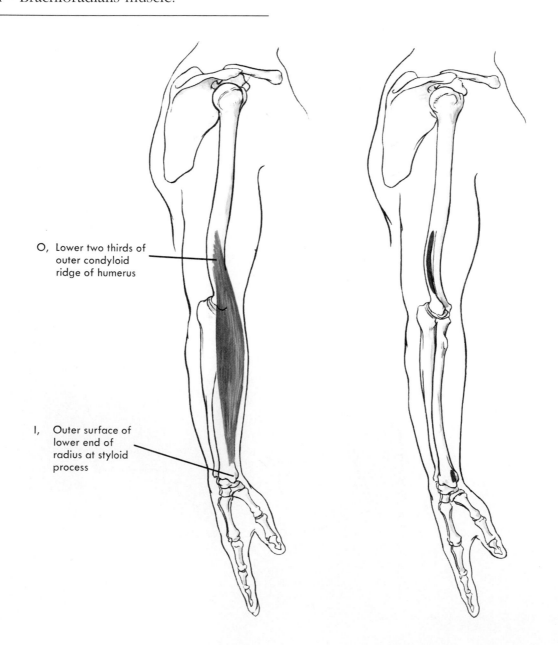

O, Lower two thirds of outer condyloid ridge of humerus

I, Outer surface of lower end of radius at styloid process

Triceps brachii muscle FIG. 4-5

Origin

Long head—lower edge of the glenoid cavity of the scapula.

Lateral head—upper half of the posterior surface of the humerus.

Medial head—lower two thirds of the posterior surface of the humerus.

Insertion

Olecranon process of the ulna.

Action

Extension of the elbow and assistance in extension of the shoulder joint (long head).

Palpation

Posterior and lateral aspects of the humerus.

Observation and exercise

Typical action of the triceps brachii is shown in push-ups when there is powerful extension of the elbow. It is used in hand balancing or in any pushing movement. The long head is an important extensor of the shoulder joint.

Two muscles extend the elbow—the triceps brachii and the anconeus. Push-ups demand strenuous contraction of these muscles. Dips on the parallel bars are more difficult to perform. Pressing a barbell or dumbbell upward with weights is an excellent exercise.

FIG. 4-5 • Triceps brachii muscle.

Modified from Anthony CP and Kolthoff NJ: Textbook of anatomy and physiology, ed. 9, St. Louis, The CV Mosby Co.

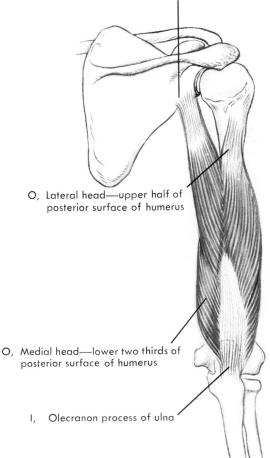

O, Long head—lower edge of glenoid cavity of scapula

O, Lateral head—upper half of posterior surface of humerus

O, Medial head—lower two thirds of posterior surface of humerus

I, Olecranon process of ulna

Anconeus muscle FIG. 4-6

Origin

Posterior surface of the external condyle of the humerus.

Insertion

Posterior surface of the upper ulna and olecranon.

Action

Extension of the elbow.

Palpation

Posterior lateral aspect of the olecranon process.

FIG. 4-6 • Anconeus muscle.

Observation and exercise

The chief function of the anconeus muscle is to pull the synovial membrane of the elbow joint out of the way of the advancing olecranon process during extension of the elbow. It contracts along with the triceps brachii.

Exercises used in the development of the triceps always call the anconeus into action.

Muscle identification

In Fig. 4-9, identify the muscles of the shoulder and elbow joint. Compare Fig. 4-9 with Fig. 4-10.

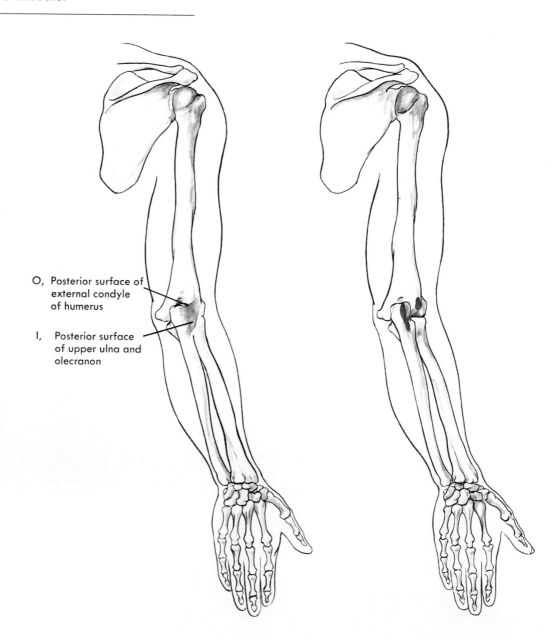

O, Posterior surface of external condyle of humerus

I, Posterior surface of upper ulna and olecranon

Supinator muscle FIG. 4-7

Origin

Outer condyloid ridge of the humerus and neighboring part of the ulna.

Insertion

Outer surface of the upper third of the radius.

Action

Supination of the elbow.

Palpation

Cannot be palpated.

Observation and exercise

The supinator muscle is called into play when the movements of extension and supination are required, such as turning a screwdriver. The out curve in throwing a baseball calls this muscle into play as the elbow is extended. Its best development takes place in movements that require supination with extension, because the biceps brachii takes care of most supination with flexion.

Grasp the hands and extend the forearm, attempting to supinate the forearms against the grip of the hands. This will localize, to a degree, the action of the supinator.

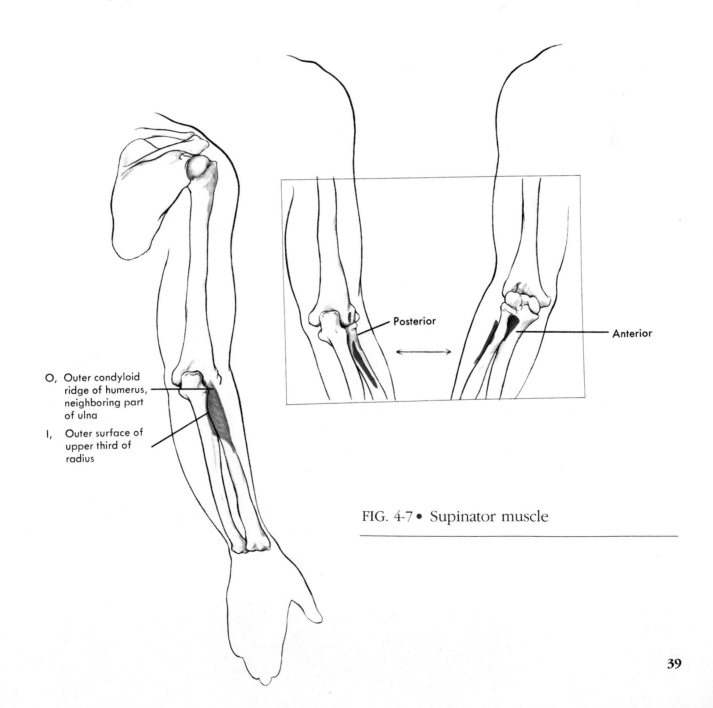

O, Outer condyloid ridge of humerus, neighboring part of ulna

I, Outer surface of upper third of radius

Posterior

Anterior

FIG. 4-7 • Supinator muscle

Pronator teres muscle FIG. 4-8

Origin

Lower part of the inner condyloid ridge of the humerus and medial side of the ulna.

Insertion

Middle third of the outer surface of the radius.

Action

Flexion of the elbow.
Pronation of the forearm.

Palpation

Cannot be palpated.

Observation

Typical movement of the pronator teres muscle is with the forearm pronating as it flexes. Movement is weaker in flexion with supination. The use of the pronator teres alone in movement would tend to bring the back of the hand to the face as it contracts.

Exercise

Pronation of the forearm with a dumbbell in the hand will localize action and develop the pronator teres muscle. Also, all elbow flexion action requires contraction of this muscle.

Pronator quadratus muscle FIG. 4-8

Origin

Lower fourth of the anterior side of the ulna.

Insertion

Lower fourth of the anterior side of the radius.

Action

Pronation of the forearm.

Palpation

Cannot be palpated.

Observation and exercise

The pronator quadratus muscle works with the triceps brachii muscle in the combined movement of extension and pronation. It is commonly used in turning a screwdriver, when extension and pronation are needed, such as in taking out a screw. It is used also in throwing a screwball, when extension and pronation are needed. It must be developed through pronated action with the triceps brachii to avoid the help of the pronator teres.

FIG. 4-8 • Pronator teres and pronator quadratus muscles.

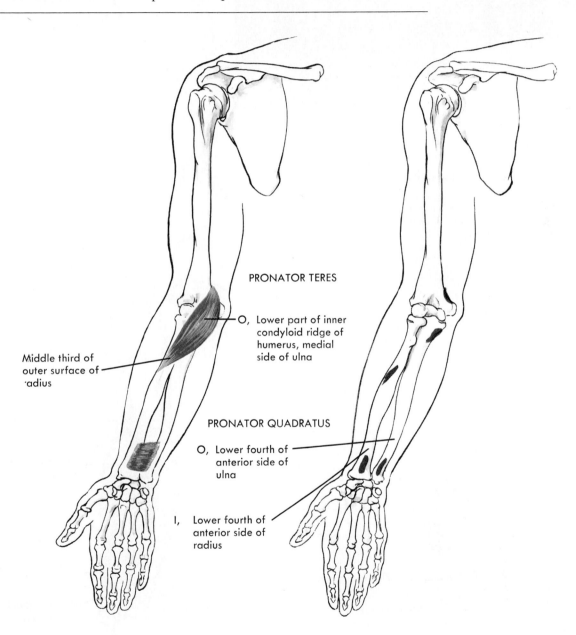

PRONATOR TERES

O, Lower part of inner
condyloid ridge of
humerus, medial
side of ulna

Middle third of
outer surface of
·adius

PRONATOR QUADRATUS

O, Lower fourth of
anterior side of
ulna

I, Lower fourth of
anterior side of
radius

FIG. 4-9 • Elbow joint muscles.

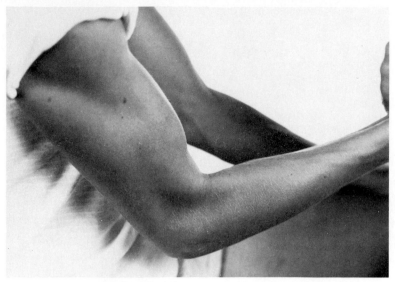

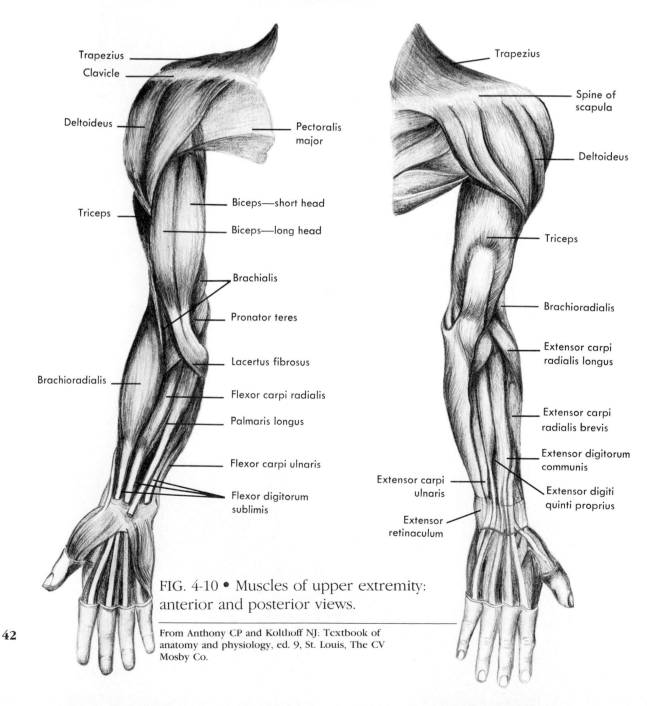

Trapezius

Clavicle

Deltoideus

Triceps

Brachioradialis

Pectoralis major

Biceps—short head

Biceps—long head

Brachialis

Pronator teres

Lacertus fibrosus

Flexor carpi radialis

Palmaris longus

Flexor carpi ulnaris

Flexor digitorum sublimis

Trapezius

Spine of scapula

Deltoideus

Triceps

Brachioradialis

Extensor carpi radialis longus

Extensor carpi radialis brevis

Extensor digitorum communis

Extensor digiti quinti proprius

Extensor carpi ulnaris

Extensor retinaculum

FIG. 4-10 • Muscles of upper extremity: anterior and posterior views.

From Anthony CP and Kolthoff NJ: Textbook of anatomy and physiology, ed. 9, St. Louis, The CV Mosby Co.

THE WRIST, HAND, AND FINGERS

Anatomically and structurally, the human wrist and hand are highly developed, complex mechanisms capable of a variety of movements, which is a result of the arrangement of the 29 bones, more than 25 joints, and more than 30 muscles.

A complete discussion of the wrist and hand is beyond the scope of this book. For the majority of students who use this text, a comprehensive knowledge of this part of the body is not essential. Therefore our consideration of this part of the body will be brief.

The muscles included will be representative muscles. *Antagonistic* muscles (flexors and extensors) are included to show opposite action.

Bones FIG. 4-11

The wrist and hand contain 29 bones, including the radius and ulna. Eight carpal bones form the wrist in two rows of four bones. Five metacarpal bones, numbered one to five from the thumb, join the wrist bones. There are 14 phalanges (digits), three for each metacarpal except the thumb, which has only two. They are indicated as proximal, middle, and distal from the metacarpals.

Movements

A more detailed consideration of the wrist and hand would include movements at the radiocarpal, carpometacarpal, and metacarpophalangeal joints. Our brief consideration will include only the following:

Flexion—pulling the palm of the hand up toward the front of the forearm.

Extension—pulling the back of the hand toward the back of the forearm.

Other movements

Movements at the wrist, fingers, and thumb include abduction, adduction, and circumduction. No consideration will be given to these movements.

Observation

The common actions of the wrist and the fingers are flexion and extension. These movements, together with pronation and supination of the forearm, make possible the many fine coordinated movements of the forearm, wrist, and hand.

Ligaments, too numerous to mention in this discussion, support and strengthen the many joints of the wrist and hand.

FIG. 4-11 • Right wrist and hand, palmar surface.

From Anthony CP and Kolthoff NJ: Textbook of anatomy and physiology, ed. 9, St. Louis, The CV Mosby Co.

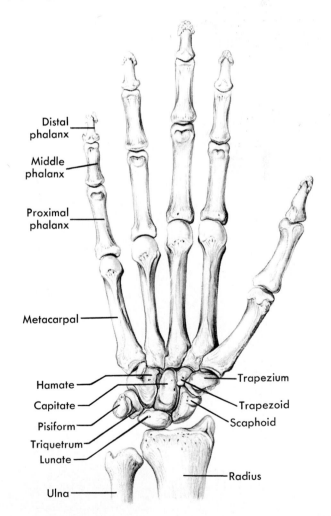

Distal phalanx
Middle phalanx
Proximal phalanx
Metacarpal
Hamate
Capitate
Pisiform
Triquetrum
Lunate
Ulna
Trapezium
Trapezoid
Scaphoid
Radius

Flexor carpi radialis muscle FIG. 4-12

Origin

Medial condyle of the humerus.

Insertion

Base of the second and the third metacarpals (palmar surface).

Action

Flexion of the wrist.
Flexion of the elbow.

Palpation

Anterior surface of the wrist, just lateral to the broad tendon.

Flexor carpi ulnaris muscle FIG. 4-12

Origin

Medial condyle of the humerus.

Insertion

Base of the fifth metacarpal.

Action

Flexion of the wrist.
Flexion of the elbow.

Palpation

Anterior surface of the forearm, a few inches below the medial epicondyle of the humerus.

FIG. 4-12 • Flexor carpi radialis (**left**) and flexor carpi ulnaris (**right**) muscles.

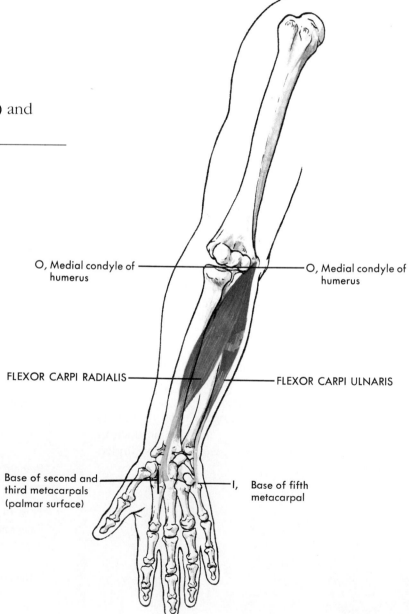

O, Medial condyle of humerus

O, Medial condyle of humerus

FLEXOR CARPI RADIALIS

FLEXOR CARPI ULNARIS

I, Base of second and third metacarpals (palmar surface)

I, Base of fifth metacarpal

Extensor carpi radialis brevis muscle FIG. 4-13

Origin

Lateral condyle of the humerus.

Insertion

Base of the third metacarpal (dorsal surface).

Action

Extension of the wrist.
Extension of the elbow.

Palpation

Dorsal side of the forearm, which is difficult to palpate.

Extensor carpi ulnaris muscle FIG. 4-13

Origin

Lateral condyle of the humerus.

Insertion

Base of the fifth metacarpal (dorsal surface).

Action

Extension of the wrist.
Adduction of the wrist together with the flexor carpi ulnaris muscle.
Extension of the forearm.

Palpation

Anterior ulnar side of the forearm near the fifth metacarpal.

FIG. 4-13 • Extensor carpi radialis brevis and extensor carpi ulnaris muscles.

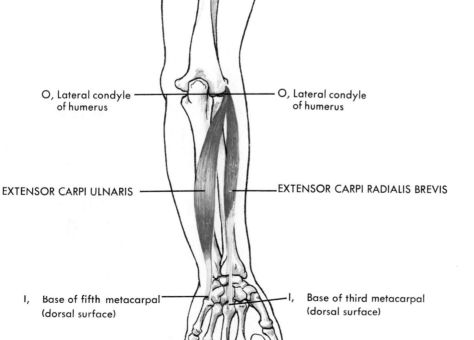

O, Lateral condyle of humerus

O, Lateral condyle of humerus

EXTENSOR CARPI ULNARIS

EXTENSOR CARPI RADIALIS BREVIS

I, Base of fifth metacarpal (dorsal surface)

I, Base of third metacarpal (dorsal surface)

Extensor digitorum communis muscle FIG. 4-14

Origin

Lateral condyle of the humerus.

Insertion

Four tendons to the bases of the second and third phalanges of the four fingers (dorsal surface).

Action

Extension of the fingers.
Extension of the wrist.
Extension of the elbow.

Palpation

Middorsal surface of the forearm.

FIG. 4-14 • Extensor digitorum communis muscle.

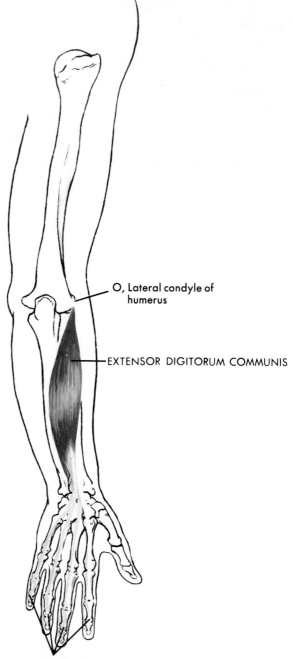

O, Lateral condyle of humerus

EXTENSOR DIGITORUM COMMUNIS

I, Four tendons to bases of second and third phalanges of four fingers (dorsal surface)

Flexor digitorum sublimis muscle

FIG. 4-14

Origin

Medial condyle of the humerus.
Ulnar head—medial coronoid area.
Radial head—radial tuberosity area.

Insertion

Split tendons attach to the sides of the middle phalanx of the four fingers (palmar surface).

Action

Flexion of the fingers.
Flexion of the wrist.
Flexion of the elbow.

Palpation

Anterior wrist surface on the ulnar side next to the flexor carpi ulnaris muscle.

FIG. 4-14, cont'd • Flexor digitorum sublimis muscle.

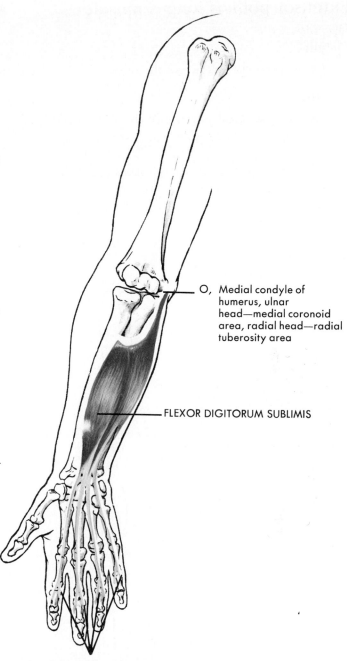

O, Medial condyle of humerus, ulnar head—medial coronoid area, radial head—radial tuberosity area

FLEXOR DIGITORUM SUBLIMIS

I, Split tendons attach to sides of middle phalanx of four fingers (palmar surface)

47

Extensor pollicis longus muscle

FIG. 4-15

Origin

Upper posterior surface of the ulna.

Insertion

Base of the distal phalanx of the thumb (dorsal surface).

FIG. 4-15 • Extensor pollicis longus and flexor pollicis longus muscles.

Action

Extension of the wrist.
Extension of the thumb.

Palpation

Most prominent on the dorsal side of the hand.

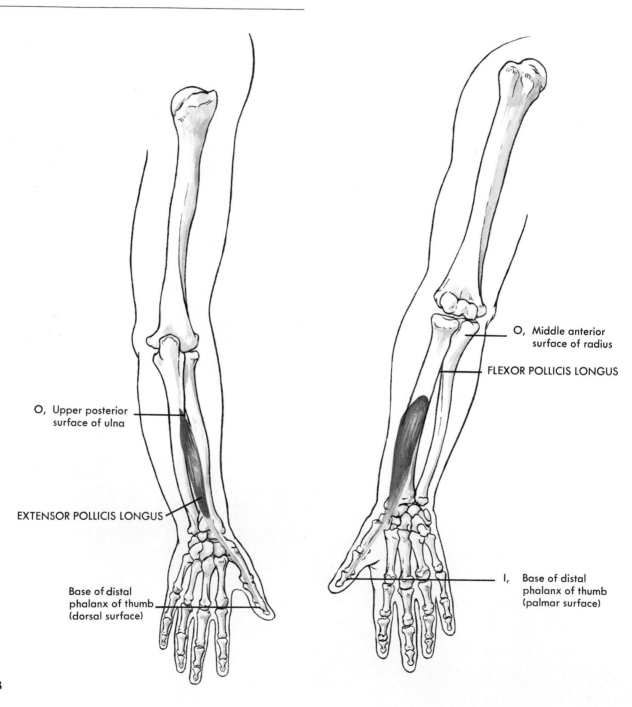

O, Upper posterior surface of ulna

EXTENSOR POLLICIS LONGUS

Base of distal phalanx of thumb (dorsal surface)

O, Middle anterior surface of radius

FLEXOR POLLICIS LONGUS

I, Base of distal phalanx of thumb (palmar surface)

48

Flexor pollicis longus muscle FIG. 4-15

Origin

Middle anterior surface of radius.

Insertion

Base of the distal phalanx of the thumb (palmar surface).

Action

Flexion of the thumb.
Flexion of the wrist.

Palpation

Cannot be palpated.

Observation and exercise

This observation applies to all muscles of the wrist, hand, and fingers. Daily use of the hands in ordinary tasks does not bring about sufficient development of these muscles, nor does the use of athletic equipment furnish enough overload to provide development. The tennis racket, golf club, football, baseball, volleyball, and so forth are lightweight. When used daily, they provide opportunity for skill but little opportunity for development. On the other hand, if activities such as chinning, climbing, and suspension of weight with the hand are indulged in, muscles of the hands are developed and strengthened. Muscles of the arms and shoulders, as well as those of the chest, are also called into strenuous action and are developed. Human beings can develop skills without having strength enough to perform well, just as they can develop strength without having skill enough to perform well.

All sports require strong hands for fine performance; therefore programs of physical education in both elementary and secondary schools should provide ample opportunity for the development of this group of muscles. Greater use of climbing apparatus, such as chinning bars, flying rings, traveling rings, climbing ropes and poles, and horizontal bars, will develop hand strength that will enable individuals to handle their own bodies effectively. This, in turn, will provide hand strength with which to perform skills in sports.

All activities in which the body weight is suspended by the hands and fingers call the wrist, hand, and finger flexors into strenuous action. Fingertip push-ups are one of the best exercises to strengthen the wrists and fingers.

Summary

A brief summary of these marvels of human engineering, found in the wrist and hand, seems to be demanded.

The movements and skills that can be performed by these parts of the human body are almost unbelievable. The anatomical arrangement of the bones, ligaments, and muscles allows for many complex and varied actions.

The most important and some representative muscles have been presented, many other small, mostly intrinsic muscles are involved:

Elbow joint flexion

All of these muscles have their origins on the humerus (radial side) and insertions on the wrist and hand. They assist in elbow joint flexion but are primarily flexors of the wrist and hand.

Flexor carpi radialis
Flexor carpi ulnaris
Palmaris longus
Flexor digitorum sublimis

Elbow joint extension

All of these muscles have their origins on the humerus (ulnar side) and insertions on the wrist and hand. They assist in elbow joint extension but are primarily extensors of the wrist and hand.

Extensor carpi radialis longus
Extensor carpi radialis brevis
Extensor digitorum communis
Extensor carpi ulnaris

Wrist and hand: flexion and extension

Flexor digitorum sublimis
Flexor digitorum profundus
Flexor pollicis longus
Extensor digitorum communis
Extensor indicis
Extensor pollicis longus
Extensor pollicis brevis

The thumb's wide range of abduction and adduction movements is very important in wrist and hand function. Many intrinsic muscles, with some assistance from extrinsic muscles, assist as primary movers.

Laboratory and review exercises

As an aid to student learning and for assignments, in-class, out-of-class, or for teacher testing, tear-out worksheets are found at the end of the text (pages 165-167).

Skeletal worksheet (no. 1)

Draw and label on the worksheet the following muscles.
(a) Bicep brachii
(b) Brachioradialis
(c) Brachialis
(d) Pronator teres
(e) Supinator
(f) Triceps brachii
(g) Anconeus

Skeletal worksheet (no. 2)

Draw and label on the worksheet the following muscles.
(a) Flexor pollicis longus
(b) Flexor carpi radialis
(c) Flexor carpi ulnaris
(d) Extensor digitorum communis
(e) Extensor pollicis longus
(f) Extensor carpi ulnaris

Human figure worksheet (no. 3)

Label and indicate by arrows the following movements of the elbow joint and wrist and hands.

Elbow joint	Wrist and hands
Flexion	Flexion
Extension	Extension
Pronation	
Supination	

Additional laboratory and review exercises

1. Locate the following parts of the humerus, radius, and ulna on a human skeleton and on a subject:
   a. Skeleton
      (1) Medial epicondyle
      (2) Lateral epicondyle
      (3) Trochlea
      (4) Capitulum
      (5) Olecranon fossa
      (6) Olecranon process
      (7) Coronoid process
      (8) Tuberosity of the radius
      (9) Styloid process—radius
      (10) Styloid process—ulna
      (11) First and third metacarpals
      (12) Wrist bones
      (13) First phalanx of third metacarpal
   b. Subject
      (1) Medial epicondyle
      (2) Lateral epicondyle
      (3) Olecranon process
2. How and where do you palpate the following muscles on a human subject?
   (a) Biceps brachii
   (b) Brachioradialis
   (c) Brachialis
   (d) Pronator teres
   (e) Supinator
   (f) Triceps brachii
   (g) Anconeus
   (h) Flexor pollicis longus
   (i) Flexor carpi radialis
   (j) Flexor carpi ulnaris
   (k) Extensor digitorum communis
   (l) Extensor pollicis longus
   (m) Extensor carpi ulnaris
3. Demonstrate the action and list the muscles primarily responsible for these movements at the elbow joint:
   (a) Flexion
   (b) Extension
   (c) Pronation
   (d) Supination
4. Discuss the difference in chinning with the palms toward the face and with the palms away from the face. Consider this muscularly and anatomically.

5. Why is the triceps brachii muscle so important in throwing? Suggest additional exercises for strengthening this muscle.
6. How would you ensure proper development of the antagonistic muscles at the elbow joint?
7. Discuss why the thumb is the most important part of the hand.
8. How should boys and girls be taught to do push-ups? Justify your answer.
   (a) Hands flat on floor
   (b) Fingertips
9. Fill in the movements and muscle actions of the elbow joint on the following chart. List the muscles primarily responsible for each movement.
10. Fill in the movements and muscle actions of the wrist and hand on the following chart. List the muscles primarily responsible for each movement.

Muscle analysis chart ● elbow

Elbow joint	
Flexion	Extension
Pronation	Supination

Muscle analysis chart ● wrist and hand

Wrist and hand	
Flexion	Extension

References

Back BR Jr, et al: Triceps rupture: a case report and literature review, American Journal of Sports Medicine 15:285, May-June 1987.

Gabbard CP, et al: Effects of grip and forearm position on flex arm hang performance, Research Quarterly for Exercise and Sport, 198, July 1983.

Herrick RT, and Herrick S: Ruptured triceps in power-lifter presenting as cubital tunnel syndrome—a case report, American Journal of Sports Medicine 15:514, September-October 1987.

Sisto DJ, et al: An electromyographic analysis of the elbow in pitching, American Journal of Sports Medicine 15:260, May-June, 1987.

Springer SI: Racquetball and elbow injuries, Nat Racq 16:7, March 1987.

Stacey E: Pitching injuries to the shoulder, Athletic Journal 64:44, January 1984.

Muscular analysis of upper extremities

5

Student objectives

• To know and understand the different types of muscle contractions.

• To learn to group individual muscles into units that produce certain joint movements.

• To begin to think of exercises that increase the strength and endurance of individual muscle groups.

• To analyze simple exercises in terms of the joint movements and muscles exercised.

The shoulder areas are the body's weakest area. American boys and girls are extremely weak in the upper shoulder area. A majority are unable to do one chin. The traditional chin-up (pull-up) has the subject grasping a horizontal bar with the feet off the floor. The body is then pulled up until the chin is over the bar. The modified chin-up (pull-up) has the feet on the floor; the subject grasps the horizontal bar and pulls the upper body up to touching the bar. The traditional chin up (pull-up) had to be modified in order to secure more meaningful results.*

Strength and endurance in this part of the human body can be increased by specific exercises and activities. To do this intelligently, one needs a thorough knowledge of the muscles involved. Everyone, young and old, needs adequate strength in this part of the body for improved appearance and posture, as well as more efficient skill performance.

At this stage, simple exercises are used to begin teaching individuals how to group muscles together to produce joint movement. For example, the most important muscles that produce elbow joint flexion are the biceps brachii, brachialis, brachioradiali, and pronator teres.

Simple introductory exercises are included in this chapter. The early analysis of exercises makes the study of structural kinesiology more meaningful as students come to better understand the importance of individual muscles and groups of muscles in bringing about joint movements in various exercises. Chapter 10 has a more comprehensive analysis of exercises for all muscle groups of the entire body. Contrary to what most beginning students in structural kinesiology believe, muscular analysis of activities is not difficult once the basic concepts are understood.

---

*Pate, R., et al: The national children and youth fitness study. II. The modified pull-up test, Journal of Physical Education, Recreation and Dance 58:71, November-December 1987.

Concepts for analysis

In the analysis of activities, it is desirable to proceed from the simple to the complex. Students understand muscles and their functioning when they are able to visualize the individual's joint movements and the primary muscles used in each movement during a given activity or exercise.

Muscle contractions can be of three types. *Concentric contraction* is the type of contraction that occurs in the shortening of a muscle. Sports activities generally involve this type of contraction. *Eccentric* (lengthening) contraction occurs when a muscle returns to its original length and is working against gravity. Both of these types of contraction are called *isotonic* contraction.

A third type of contraction is *isometric* (static) contraction. This is contraction with little or no shortening of the muscle. It is a very effective way to increase muscle strength but improves strength only at the angle of contraction.

The recent development of exercise machines has resulted in another type of contraction known as *isokinetic* contraction. This is a contraction that has a constant force or speed throughout the range of movement. Nautilus, Cybex, and other new types of apparatus are engineered to allow this type of contraction.

Well-trained students in kinesiology should be qualified to prescribe exercises and activities for the development of large muscles and muscle groups in the human body. They should be able to read the description of an exercise or observe an exercise and immediately know the most important muscles that are being used. In addition, they should be able to point out the muscle group that is being used most strenuously in an exercise. The more opportunity students have to analyze exercises and activities, the more proficient they will become.

From a practical point of view, it is not essential individuals know the exact force exerted by each of the forearm flexors in chinning—biceps, brachialis, brachioradialis, and pronator teres. It is important to understand that this muscle group is responsible for elbow joint flexion, that these muscles contract concentrically when the chin is pulled up to the bar, and that they contract eccentrically when the body is lowered. Antagonistic muscles are muscles that produce opposite actions (flexion-extension). For example, the muscles that produce flexion of the elbow joint are antagonistic to the muscles that produce extension of the elbow joint. It is important to understand that specific exercises need to be given for the development of each antagonistic muscle group. The return movement to the hanging position at the elbow joint after chinning is elbow joint extension, but the triceps and anconeus are not being strengthened. It is concentric and eccentric contraction of the elbow joint flexors.

In recent years the practice of stretching muscles has been emphasized as a way to help prevent injuries. It is easy to put a muscle on a stretch if one knows its origin and insertion.

In a review of structural kinesiology with graduate physical education teachers and coaches, I have found that this practical knowledge is often lacking. In fact, some individuals believe pronation of the forearm when chinning (palms away) brings the triceps into strong contraction rather than the biceps. This erroneous belief, and many others that could be mentioned, indicates a serious lack of knowledge in this area.

How can individuals prescribe exercises for the (muscular) system when they lack this knowledge and understanding? The answer is obvious: it is impossible.

The analysis of activities and exercises may be brief or detailed. The analyses used in this chapter are considered to be detailed. The muscles indicated are the most important movers of the joints. Slight movements of the body parts unrelated to the primary movement being analyzed are generally not considered. Any analysis of muscular activity, of necessity, must be somewhat limited.

Upper extremity activities

Children seem to have an innate desire to climb, swing, and hang. Such movements use the muscles of the hands, wrists, elbows, and shoulder joints. But the opportunity to perform these types of activities is limited in our modern culture. Unless emphasis is placed on the development of this area of our bodies by physical education teachers in elementary schools, for both boys and girls, it will continue to be muscularly the weakest area of our bodies. Boys and girls enjoy what they can do well, and they can be taught to enjoy activities that will increase the strength of this part of the body.

Chin-up (pull-up) FIG. 5-1

Description

The subject grasps a horizontal bar or ladder with the palms toward the face. From a hanging position on the bar, she pulls up until her chin is over the bar. Then she returns to the starting position.

Analysis

This exercise is separated into two movements for analysis: (1) movement upward to chinning position and (2) return movement to hanging position.

Movement upward to chinning position
  Wrist and hand
    Flexion
      Wrist and hand flexors
  Elbow joint
    Flexion
      Biceps brachii
      Brachialis
      Brachioradialis
      Pronator teres

  Shoulder joint
    Extension
      Latissimus dorsi
      Teres major
      Posterior deltoideus
      Pectoralis major
      Triceps brachii (long head)
  Shoulder girdle
    Adduction and depression
      Trapezius (lower)
      Pectoralis minor

Return movement to hanging position
  Wrist and hand
    Flexion
      Wrist and hand flexors
  Elbow joint
    Extension
      Elbow joint flexors (eccentric contraction)
  Shoulder joint
    Flexion
      Shoulder joint extensors (eccentric contraction)
  Shoulder girdle
    Elevation and abduction
      Trapezius (eccentric contraction)
      Pectoralis minor (eccentric contraction)

FIG. 5-1 • Pull-up. **A,** Straight-arm hang. **B,** Chin over bar. **C,** Bent-arm hang on way up or down.

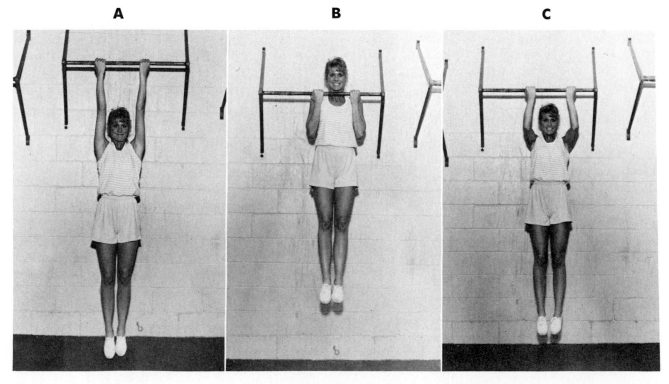

A   **B**   **C**

Push-up (fingertip) FIG. 5-2

Description

The subject lies on the floor in a prone position with the legs together and the fingertips touching the floor with the hands pointed forward and approximately under the shoulders. Keeping the back and legs straight, the subject pushes up to a front-leaning rest position and returns to the starting position.

Analysis

This exercise is separated into two movements for analysis: (1) movement to front-leaning rest position and (2) return movement to starting position.

Movement to front-leaning rest position
  Wrist and hand
    Isometric contraction of wrist and hand flexors and extensors
  Elbow joint
    Extension
      Triceps brachii
      Anconeus

Shoulder joint
  Flexion
    Pectoralis major
    Anterior deltoideus
    Biceps brachii
Shoulder girdle
  Abduction
    Serratus anterior
    Pectoralis minor

Return movement to starting position
  Wrist and hand
    Isometric contraction of wrist and hand flexors and extensors
  Elbow joint
    Flexion
      Elbow joint extensors (eccentric contraction)
  Shoulder joint
    Extension
      Shoulder joint flexors (eccentric contraction)
  Shoulder girdle
    Adduction
      Shoulder girdle abductors (eccentric contraction)

Chins and push-ups are excellent exercises for the shoulder area, shoulder girdle, shoulder joint, elbow joint, and wrist and hand (Fig. 5-2). Other exercises for this area are considered in Chapter 10. The use of weights, Universal conditioning machine, and conditioning exercises will help develop strength and endurance for this part of the body.

FIG. 5-2 • Push-up. **A**, Starting position. **B**, Front-leaning rest position.

Latissimus pull (lats pull) FIG. 5-3

Description

From a sitting position the subject reaches up and grasps a horizontal bar (Fig. 5-3) at shoulder width apart. The bar is pulled down to a position behind the shoulders. Then it is returned to the starting position.

Analysis

This exercise is separated into two movements for analysis: (1) movement downward to a position behind the shoulders and (2) return to the starting position.

Movement downward to position behind the shoulders
- Wrist and hands
  - Flexion
    - Wrist and hand flexors
- Elbow joint
  - Flexion
    - Biceps brachii
    - Brachialis
    - Brachioradialis
    - Pronator teres

Shoulder joint
- Adduction
  - Pectoralis major
  - Anterior deltoid
  - Latissimus dorsi
  - Teres major
- **Shoulder girdle**
  - Adduction and depression
    - Trapezius (lower)
    - Rhomboidus
    - Pectoralis minor

Return to the starting position
- **Wrist and hand**
  - Wrist and hand flexors
- **Elbow joint**
  - Extension
    - Elbow joint flexors (eccentric contraction)
- **Shoulder joint**
  - Abduction and Elevation
    - Shoulder joint adductors (eccentric contraction)
- **Shoulder girdle**
  - Abduction and elevation
    - Shoulder girdle adductors (eccentric contraction)

FIG. 5-3 • Latissimus pull (lats pull). **A**, Starting position. **B**, Downward position.

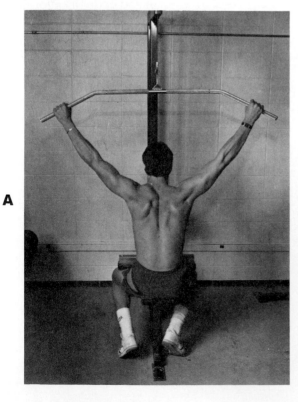
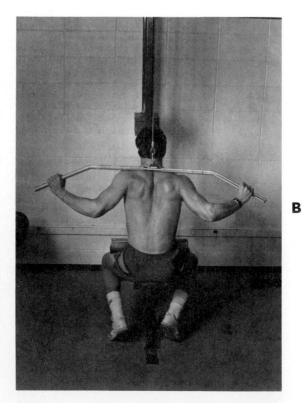

Laboratory and review exercises

As an aid to student learning and for assignments, in-class, out of class, or for teacher testing, a tear-out worksheet is found at the end of the text (page 169).

Dip exercise worksheet (no. 1)

Analyze this exercise following the procedure explained in this chapter that includes joint movements and muscles that produce these movements.

Additional laboratory and review exercises

1. Analyze other conditioning exercises that involve the shoulder area.
2. Observe and analyze shoulder muscular activities of children on playground apparatus.
3. Discuss how you would teach boys and girls who cannot chin to learn to chin. To do more push-ups.
4. Should boys and girls do chins and push-ups in the same way? Defend your answer.
5. Test yourself doing chins and push-ups to see whether you have adequate strength in this area of the body.
6. Why are push-ups better when done from the fingertips than with the hands flat on the floor?
7. Refer to physical fitness test norms to see what are reasonable levels of achievement in chins and push-ups for different age levels (boys and girls).

References

Bouche J: Three essential lifts for high school players, Scholastic Coach 56:42, April 1987.

Brzycki M: ℞ for a safe productive strength program, Scholastic Coach 57:70, September 1987.

Epley B: Getting elementary muscles, Coach and Athlete, 44:60, November-December, 1981.

Matheson O, et al: Stress fractures in athletes, American Journal of Sports Medicine, 15:46, January-February 1987.

Schlitz J: The athlete's daily dozen stretches, Athletic Journal 66:20, November 1985.

The hip joint and pelvic girdle

6

Student objectives

• To identify on a human skeleton or living subject the most important bone features of the hip joint and pelvic girdle.

• To label on a skeletal chart the most important bone features of the hip joint and pelvic girdle.

• To draw on a skeletal chart the individual muscles of the hip joint.

• To demonstrate with a fellow student all the movements of the hip joint and pelvic girdle.

• To palpate on a human subject the muscles of the hip joint and pelvic girdle.

• To list and organize the primary muscles that produce movements of the hip joint and pelvic girdle.

FIG. 6-1 • Right pelvic bone.

From Anthony CP and Kolthoff NJ: Textbook of anatomy and physiology, ed. 9, St. Louis, The CV Mosby Co.

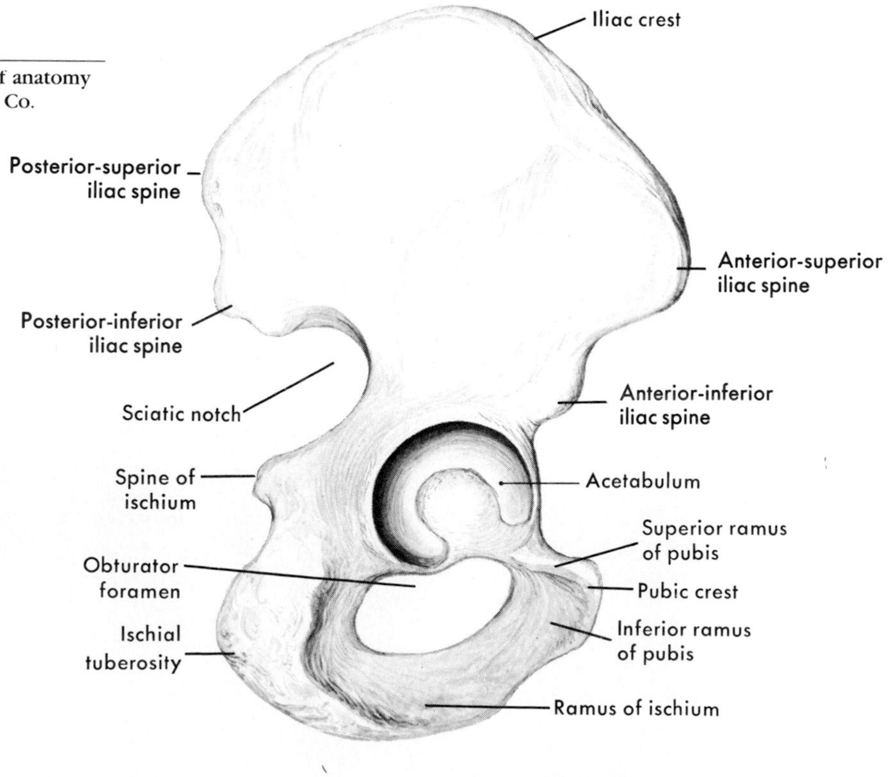

The hip joint and pelvic girdle include the two pelvic bones, the sacrum, and two femur bones. The sacrum can be considered an extension of the spinal column with five fused vertebrae. The pelvic bones are made up of three bones: ilium, ischium, and pubis bones. At birth and during growth and development they are three distinct bones. At maturity they are fused to form one pelvic bone.

The pelvic bone can be roughly divided into three areas from the acetabulum:

Upper two fifths = ilium
Posterior and lower two fifths = ischium
Anterior and lower one fifth = pubis

Bones (FIGS. 6-1 to 6-3)

In the anterior area, the pelvic bones are joined together to form the symphisis pubis, an immovable joint. In the posterior area the sacrum is located between the two pelvic bones and forms the sacroiliac joints. Strong ligaments unite these bones and form rigid, immovable joints. The bones are large and heavy and for the most part are covered by thick, heavy muscles. Isolated joint movements can occur in this area. A good example is hip flexion when lying on one's back. However, movements usually involve the entire pelvic girdle and hip joints. In walking there is hip flexion and extension with rotation of the pelvic girdle, forward in hip flexion and backward in hip extension. Jogging and running result in faster and greater range of these movements.

Sport skills, such as kicking a football or soccer ball, are other good examples of hip and pelvic movements. Pelvic rotation helps increase the length of the stride in running; in kicking it results in a greater distance or more speed to the kick.

At the hip joint there are six two-joint muscles that have one action at the hip and another at the knee.

FIG. 6-2 • Hip and pelvic bones—anterior view.

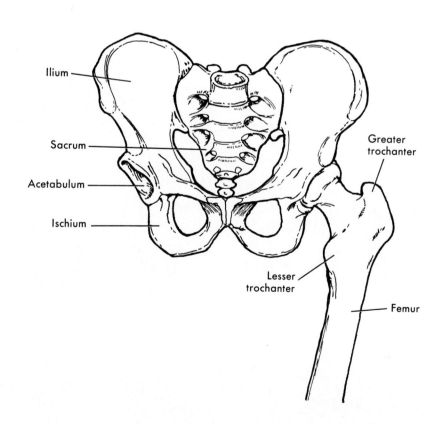

Ilium

Sacrum

Acetabulum

Ischium

Greater trochanter

Lesser trochanter

Femur

Movements

Hip Flexion—movement of the femur forward on the pelvis.

Hip horizontal flexion—forward movement in horizontal plane from abducted position.

Hip extension—return from flexion.

Hip horizontal extension—sideward movement in a horizontal plane from adducted position.

Hip abduction—movement of femur to the side.

Hip adduction—return from abduction to the original position.

Hip rotation outward—movement of the femur outward.

Hip rotation inward—return to the original position.

Pelvic girdle—rotation to right or left.

Pelvic girdle—lateral tilt to right or left.

Pelvic girdle—slight forward or backward movement.

Observation

The flexor muscles are used in lifting the legs, but the extensor muscles are used eccentrically when the pelvis and the trunk move downward on the femur and concentrically when the trunk is raised on the femur—this, of course, in the standing position.

In the knee-bend exercise the movement at hips and knees is flexion. The muscles involved primarily are the hip and knee extensors in eccentric contraction.

Hip joint and pelvic girdle muscles—location

Muscle location largely determines the muscle action. Sixteen or more muscles are found in this area (the six outward rotators are counted as one muscle). Most hip joint and pelvic girdle muscles are large and strong.

Anterior
Primarily hip flexion
Iliopsoas
Pectineus
Rectus femoris*
Sartorius
Tensor fasciae latae

Medial
Primarily hip adduction
Adductor brevis
Adductor longus
Adductor magnus
Gracilis

Posterior
Primarily hip extension
Gluteus maximus
Biceps femoris*
Semitendinosus*
Semimembraneous*
Outward rotators

Lateral
Primarily hip abduction
Gluteus medius
Gluteus minimus
Outward rotators

---

*Two-joint muscles; knee actions will be discussed in Chapter 7.

FIG. 6-3 • Right femur, anterior surface.

From Anthony CP and Kolthoff NJ: Textbook of anatomy and physiology, ed. 9, St. Louis, The CV Mosby Co.

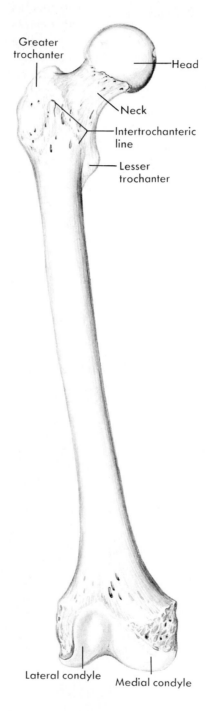

Iliopsoas muscle FIG. 6-4

Origin

Inner surface of the ilium, base of the sacrum, and sides of the bodies of the last thoracic and all the lumbar vertebrae.

Insertion

Lesser trochanter of the femur and shaft just below.

Action

Flexion of the hip.
Outward rotation of the femur.
When the thigh is fixed, the iliopsoas muscle pulls on the vertebrae and flexes the spine and pelvis on the thigh, as in rising to a sitting position from the supine position.

Palpation

Impossible to palpate except with almost complete relaxation of the rectus abdominis muscle.

Observation and exercise

The iliopsoas muscle is powerful in actions such as raising thelegs from a supine position on the floor. Its origin in the lower back tends to move the lower back inward or, in the supine position, pulls the lower back up as it raises the legs. For this reason, lower back strains are felt many times in this activity. The abdominals are the muscles that can be used to prevent this lower back strain by pulling uip on the front of the pelvis and thus flattening the back. Leg raising is primarily hip flexion and not abdominal action. Backs may be injured by strenuous and prolonged leg-raising exercises. The iliopsoas contracts strongly, both concentrically and eccentrically, in sit-ups, particularly if the hip is not flexed. Some anatomy books list this muscle as two muscles: iliacus and psoas.

The iliopsoas is exercised by raising and lowering the legs while lying on the back. Running activities, especially running with the legs lifted high, develop this muscle.

FIG. 6-4 • Iliopsoas muscle.

Modified from Anthony CP and Kolthoff NJ: Textbook of anatomy and physiology, ed. 9, St. Louis, The CV Mosby Co.

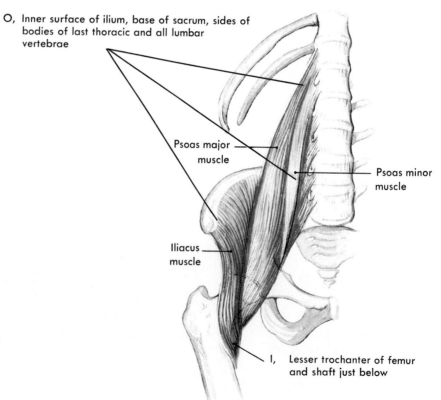

O, Inner surface of ilium, base of sacrum, sides of bodies of last thoracic and all lumbar vertebrae

Psoas major muscle

Psoas minor muscle

Iliacus muscle

I, Lesser trochanter of femur and shaft just below

Sartorius muscle FIG. 6-5

Origin

Notch between the anterior-superior and anterior-inferior spines of the ilium.

Insertion

Anterior medial condyle of the tibia.

Action

Flexion of the hip.
Flexion of the knee.
Rotation of the thigh outward as it flexes the hip and knee.

Palpation

Easiest to palpate at the anterior-superior spine of the ilium; impossible to palpate on subjects with medium and heavy legs.

Observation and exercise

Pulling from the notch between the anterior-superior and the anterior-inferior spines of the ilium, the tendency again is to tilt the pelvis down in front as this muscle contracts. The abdominal muscles must prevent this tendency by pulling up in front and thus flattening the lower back.

The sartorius, being a two-joint muscle, is effective as a hip flexor or as a knee flexor. It is weak when both actions take place at the same time. Observe that, in attempting to cross the knees when in a sitting position, one customarily leans well back, thus raising the origin of this muscle, making it more effective in flexing and crossing the knees. With the knees held extended, the sartorius becomes a more effective hip flexor. It is exercised effectively in raising the body to a sitting position from the supine position while holding the knees extended.

FIG. 6-5 • Sartorius muscle.

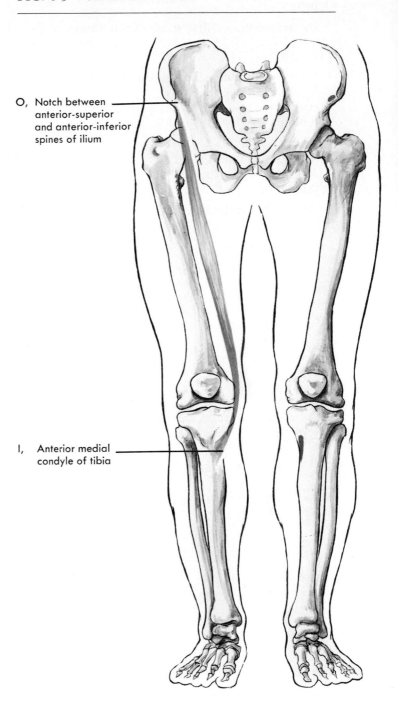

O, Notch between anterior-superior and anterior-inferior spines of ilium

I, Anterior medial condyle of tibia

63

Rectus femoris muscle FIG. 6-6

Origin

Anterior-inferior iliac spine of the ilium.

Insertion

Top of the patella and patellar ligament to the tibial tuberosity.

Action

Flexion of the hip.
Extension of the knee.

Palpation

Any place on the anterior surface of the femur.

Observation and exercise

Pulling from the anterior-inferior iliac spine of the ilium, the rectus femoris muscle has the same tendency to pull the pelvis down in front and up in back. Only the abdominal muscles can prevent this from occurring. In speaking of the hip flexor group in general, it may be said that many persons permit the pelvis to be permanently tilted forward as they get older. The relaxed abdominal wall does not hold the pelvis up, and therefore an increased lumbar curve results.

The rectus femoris muscle is a powerful extensor of the knee when the hip is extended but is weak when the hip is flexed. This muscle therefore is exercised, along with the vastus group, in running, jumping, hopping, and skipping. In these movements the hips are extended powerfully by the gluteus maximus and the hamstring muscles, which counteract the tendency of the rectus femoris muscle to flex the hip while it extends the knee. It can be remembered as one of the quadriceps muscle group.

FIG. 6-6 • Rectus femoris muscle.

Modified from Anthony CP and Kolthoff NJ: Textbook of anatomy and physiology, ed. 9, St. Louis, The CV Mosby Co.

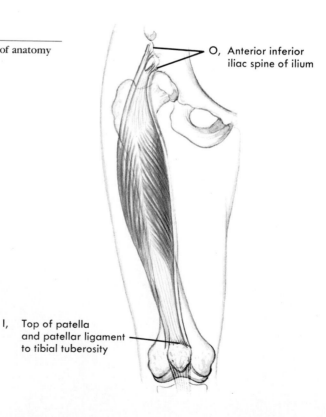

O, Anterior inferior iliac spine of ilium

I, Top of patella and patellar ligament to tibial tuberosity

Tensor fasciae latae muscle FIG. 6-7

Origin

Anterior iliac crest and surface of the ilium just below the crest.

Insertion

Iliotibial band of fascia on the thigh one fourth of the way down.

Action

Flexion of the hip.
Horizontal abduction of the hip.
Tendency to rotate hip inward as it flexes.

Palpation

Slightly in front of the greater trochanter.

Observation and exercise

The tensor fasciae latae muscle aids in preventing outward rotation of the femur as it is flexed by other flexor muscles.

The tensor fasciae latae muscle is used when flexion and inward rotation take place. This is a weak movement but important in helping to direct the leg forward so that the foot is placed straight forward in walking and running. Thus, from the supine position, raising the leg with definite inward rotation of the femur will call it into action.

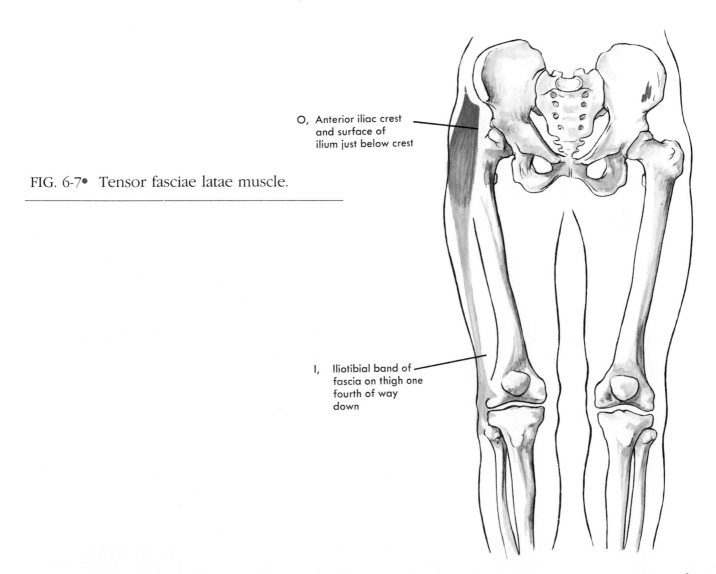

O, Anterior iliac crest and surface of ilium just below crest

I, Iliotibial band of fascia on thigh one fourth of way down

FIG. 6-7• Tensor fasciae latae muscle.

Gluteus medius muscle FIG. 6-8

Origin

Outer surface of the ilium just below the crest.

Insertion

Posterior and middle surfaces of the greater trochanter of the femur.

Action

Abduction of the hip.
Rotation outward as the hip abducts (posterior fibers).

Palpation

Slightly in front of and a few inches above the greater trochanter.

Observation and exercise

See p. 67

FIG. 6-8 • Gluteus medius muscle.

Modified from Anthony CP and Kolthoff NJ: Textbook of anatomy and physiology, ed. 9, St. Louis, The CV Mosby Co.

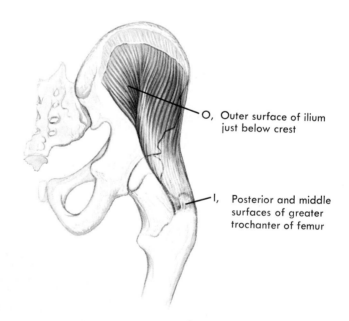

O, Outer surface of ilium just below crest

I, Posterior and middle surfaces of greater trochanter of femur

Gluteus minimus muscle FIG. 6-9

Origin

Outer surface of the ilium below the origin of the gluteus medius.

Insertion

Anterior surface of the greater trochanter of the femur.

Action

Abduction of the femur on the pelvis.
Rotation inward as the femur abducts.

Palpation

Cannot be palpated.

Observation and exercise

Typical action of the gluteus medius and gluteus minimus muscles is seen in walking. As the weight of the body is suspended on one leg, these muscles prevent the opposite hip from sagging. They are more powerfully used in the same action in running. To have great drive in the legs, these muscles must be fully developed.

As the body ages, the gluteus medius and gluteus minimus muscles tend to lose their effectiveness. The spring of youth, as far as the hips are concerned, resides in these muscles. They are exercised effectively in running, hopping, and skipping, where weight is transferred forcefully from one foot to the other.

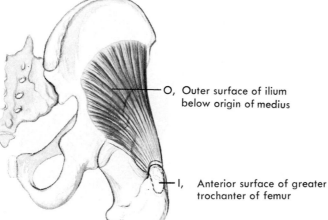

O, Outer surface of ilium below origin of medius

I, Anterior surface of greater trochanter of femur

FIG. 6-9 • Gluteus minimus muscle.

Modified from Anthony CP and Kolthoff NJ: Textbook of anatomy and physiology, ed. 9, St. Louis, The CV Mosby Co.

Gluteus maximus muscle FIG. 6-10

Origin

Posterior one fourth of the crest of the ilium, posterior surface of the sacrum near the ilium, and fascia of the lumbar area.

Insertion

Gluteal line of femur and iliotibial band of fascia latae.

Action

Extension of the hip.
Outward rotation of the hip.
Lower fibers, which assist in adduction.

Palpation

Wide area on the posterior surface of the pelvis.

Observation and exercise

The gluteus maximus muscle comes into action when movement between the pelvis and femur approaches and goes beyond 15 degrees of extension. It should not be used extensively in ordinary walking. It is important in extension of the thigh with outward rotation.

Strong action of the gluteus maximus muscle is seen in running, hopping, skipping, and jumping. Powerful extension of the thigh is secured in the return to standing from a squatting position, especially if a barbell with weights is placed on the shoulders.

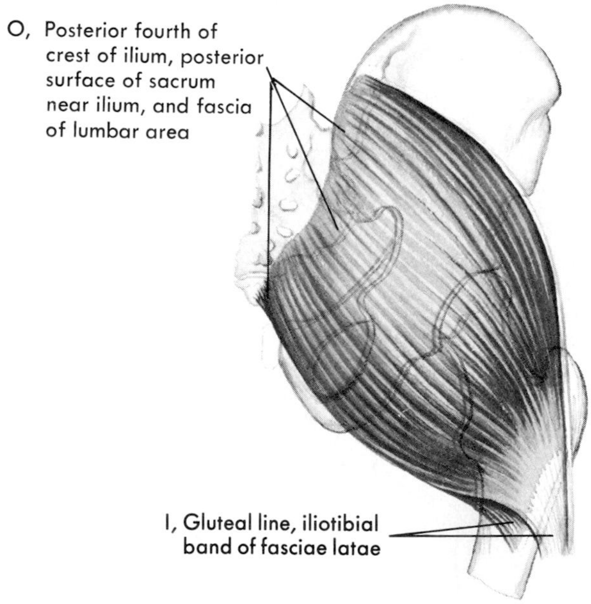

FIG. 6-10 • Gluteus maximus muscle.

Modified from Anthony CP, and Kolthoff NJ: Textbook of anatomy and physiology, ed. 9, St. Louis, The CV Mosby Co.

O, Posterior fourth of crest of ilium, posterior surface of sacrum near ilium, and fascia of lumbar area

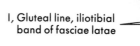

I, Gluteal line, iliotibial band of fasciae latae

Six deep lateral rotator muscles—piriformis, gemellus superior, gemellus inferior, obturator externus, obturator internus, and quadratus femoris FIG. 6-11

Origin

Sacrum, posterior portions of the ischium, and obturator foramen.

Insertion

Greater trochanter and posterior aspect of the greater trochanter.

Action

Outward rotation.

Palpation

Cannot be palpated.

Observation and exercise

The six lateral rotators are used powerfully in movements of lateral rotation of the femur, as in sports in which the individual takes off on one leg from a preliminary inward rotation. Throwing a baseball and swinging a baseball bat, in which there is rotation of the hip, are typical examples.

While standing on one leg, forcefully turn the body laterally from the femur. Repeat on the other leg.

FIG. 6-11 • Six deep outward rotator muscles: piriformis, gemellus superior, gemellus inferior, obturator externus, obturator internus, and quadratus femoris.

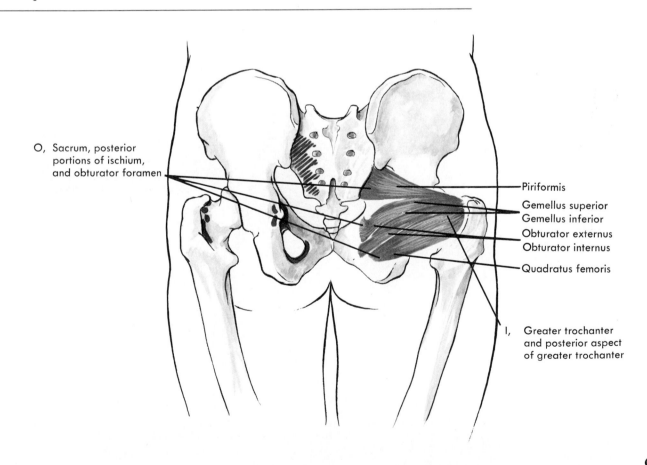

O, Sacrum, posterior portions of ischium, and obturator foramen

Piriformis
Gemellus superior
Gemellus inferior
Obturator externus
Obturator internus
Quadratus femoris

I, Greater trochanter and posterior aspect of greater trochanter

Biceps femoris muscle FIG. 6-12

Origin

Tuberosity of the ischium, lower half of the linea aspera, and outer condyloid ridge.

Insertion

Lateral condyle of the tibia and head of the fibula.

Action

Extension of the hip.
Flexion of the knee.
Outward rotation of the hip and knee.

Palpation

Lateral posterior side of the femur, near the knee.

Observation and exercise

The semitendinosus, semimembranosus, and biceps femoris muscles are known as the hamstrings. These muscles, together with the gluteus maximus muscle, are used in extension of the thigh when the knees are straight or nearly so. Thus in running, jumping, skipping, and hopping, these muscles are used together. The hamstrings are used without the aid of the gluteus maximus, however, when one is hanging from a bar by the knees. Similarly, the gluteus maximus is used without the aid of the hamstrings when the knees are bent while the hips are being extended. This occurs when rising from a knee-bend position to the standing position.

FIG. 6-12 • Biceps femoris muscle.

Modified from Anthony CP, and Kolthoff NJ: Textbook of anatomy and physiology, ed. 9, St. Louis, The CV Mosby Co.

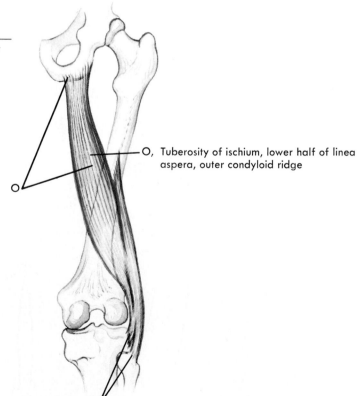

O, Tuberosity of ischium, lower half of linea aspera, outer condyloid ridge

I, Lateral condyle of tibia, head of fibula

Semitendinosus muscle FIG. 6-13

Origin

Tuberosity of the ischium.

Insertion

Upper anterior medial condyle of the tibia.

Action

Extension of the hip.
Flexion of the knee.
Inward rotation of the hip and knee.

Palpation

Near the knee on the posterior-medial side.

Observation and exercise

This two-joint muscle is most effective when contracting separately, either at the hip joint in extension or at the knee joint in flexion. When there is extension of the hip and flexion of the knee at the same time, both movements are weak. When the trunk is bent forward with the knees straight, the hamstring muscles have a powerful pull on the rear pelvis and tilt it down in back by full contraction. If the knees are flexed when this movement takes place, one can observe that the work is done chiefly by the gluteus maximus muscle.

On the other hand, when the muscles are used in powerful flexion of the knees, as in hanging by the knees from a bar, the flexors of the hip come into action to raise the origin of these muscles and make them more effective as knee flexors. By full extension of the hips in this movement, the knee flexion movement is weakened. These muscles are used in ordinary walking as extensors of the hip and allow the gluteus maximus to relax in the movement.

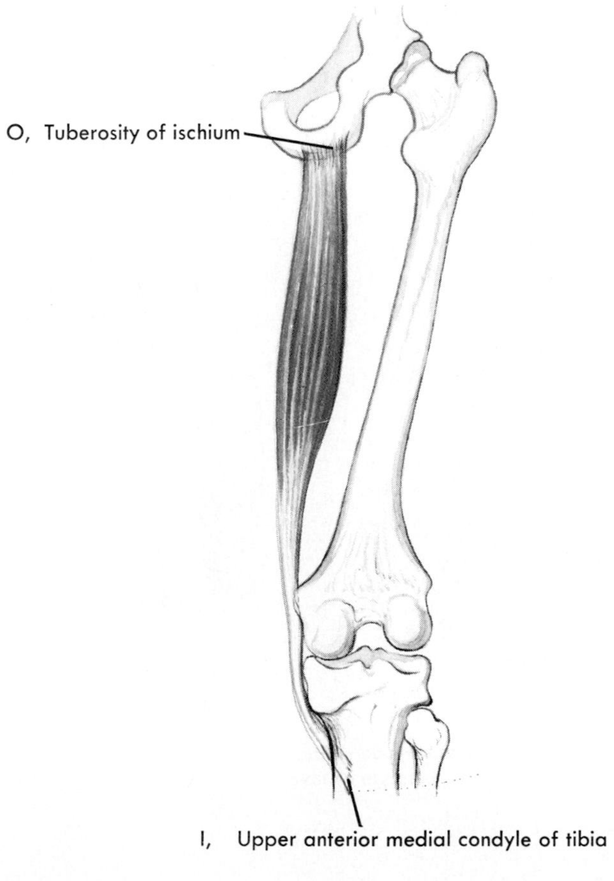

O, Tuberosity of ischium

I, Upper anterior medial condyle of tibia

FIG. 6-13 • Semitendinosus muscle.

Modified from Anthony CP and Kolthoff NJ: Textbook of anatomy and physiology, ed. 9, St. Louis, The CV Mosby Co.

Semimembranosus muscle FIG. 6-14

Origin

Tuberosity of the ischium.

Insertion

Posterior surface medial condyle of the tibia.

Action

Extension of the hip.
Flexion of the knee.
Inward rotation of the hip and knee.

Palpation

Largely covered by other muscles, the tendon can be felt at the posterior aspect of the tibia on the medial side.

Observation and exercise

See p. 70.

FIG. 6-14 • Semimembranosus muscle.

Modified from Anthony CP and Kolthoff NJ: Textbook of anatomy and physiology, ed. 9, St. Louis, The CV Mosby Co.

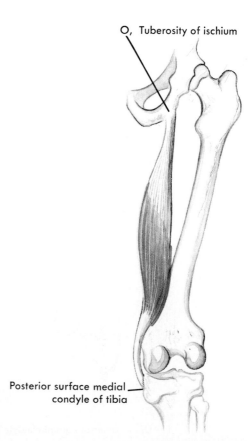

O, Tuberosity of ischium

I, Posterior surface medial condyle of tibia

Pectineus muscle FIG. 6-15

Origin

Space 1 inch wide on the front of the pubis just above the crest.

Insertion

Rough line leading from the lesser trochanter down to the linea aspera.

Action

Flexion of the hip.
Adduction of the hip on the pelvis.

Palpation

Angle between the pubic bone and the femur; hard to distinguish from the adductor longus muscle.

Observation and exercise

As the pectineus contracts, it also tends to tilt the pelvis down in front and up in back. The abdominal muscles, pulling up on the pelvis in front, prevent this tilting action.

The pectineus muscle is exercised together with the iliopsoas muscle in leg raising and lowering.

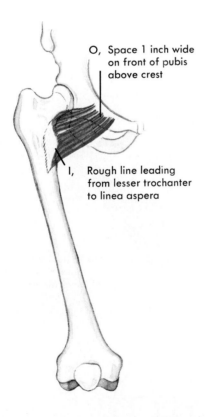

O, Space 1 inch wide on front of pubis above crest

I, Rough line leading from lesser trochanter to linea aspera

FIG. 6-15 • Pectineus muscle.

Modified from Anthony CP and Kolthoff NJ: Textbook of anatomy and physiology, ed. 9, St. Louis, The CV Mosby Co.

Adductor brevis muscle FIG. 6-16

Origin

Front of the pubis just below the origin of the longus.

Insertion

Lesser trochanter and upper one fourth of the linea aspera.

Action

Adduction of the hip.
Rotation outward as it adducts the hip.

Palpation

Cannot be palpated.

Observation and exercise

See p. 79.

FIG. 6-16 • Adductor brevis muscle.

Modified from Anthony CP and Kolthoff NJ: Textbook of anatomy and physiology, ed. 9, St. Louis, The CV Mosby Co.

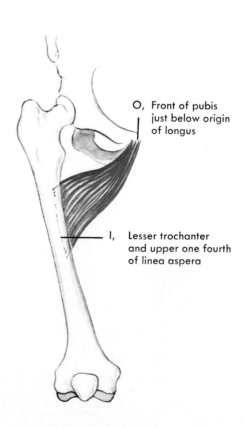

O, Front of pubis just below origin of longus

I, Lesser trochanter and upper one fourth of linea aspera

Adductor longus muscle FIG. 6-17

Origin

Front of the pubis just below its crest.

Insertion

Middle third of the linea aspera.

Action

Adduction of the hip.
Assists in flexion of the hip.

Palpation

Just below the pubic bone on the medial side.

Observation and exercise

See p. 79.

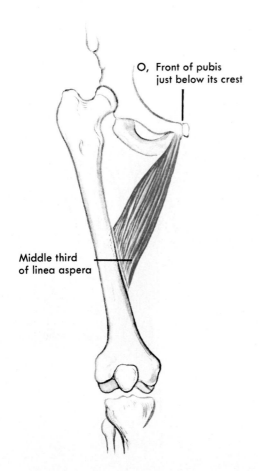

O, Front of pubis
just below its crest

Middle third
of linea aspera

FIG. 6-17 • Adductor longus muscle.

Modified from Anthony CP and Kolthoff, NJ: Textbook of anatomy and physiology, ed. 9, St. Louis, The CV Mosby Co.

75

Adductor magnus muscle FIG. 6-18

Origin

Edge of the entire ramus of the pubis and the ischium and tuberosity of the ischium.

Insertion

Whole length of the linea aspera and inner condyloid ridge.

Action

Adduction of the hip.
Rotation outward as the hip adducts.

Palpation

Posterior-medial surface of the thigh.

Observation and exercise

The adductor magnus muscle is used in the breaststroke kick in swimming or in horseback riding. Since the adductor muscles (adductor magnus, adductor longus, adductor brevis, and gracilis muscles) are not used in ordinary movement, some prescribed activity for them should be provided. Some modern exercise equipment includes a machine engineered with resistance for hip adduction movement.

FIG. 6-18 • Adductor magnus muscle.

Modified from Anthony CP and Kolthoff NJ: Textbook of anatomy and physiology, ed. 9, St. Louis, The CV Mosby Co.

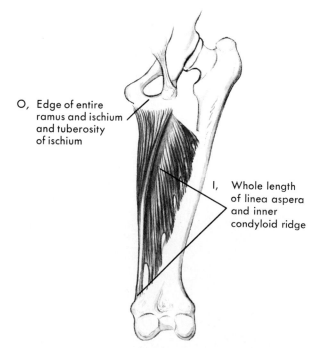

O, Edge of entire ramus and ischium and tuberosity of ischium

I, Whole length of linea aspera and inner condyloid ridge

Gracilis muscle FIG. 6-19

Origin

Inner edge of the descending ramus of the pubis.

Insertion

Anterior medial surface of tibia below the condyle.

Action

Adduction of the hip.
Flexion of the knee.
Inward rotation of the hip.

Palpation

Medial side of the thigh 2 to 3 inches below the pubic bone.

Observation and exercise

The gracilis muscle performs the same function as the other adductors but adds the movement of knee flexion.

The adductor muscles as a group (adductor magnus, adductor longus, adductor brevis, and gracilis) are called into action in horseback riding and in doing the breaststroke kick in swimming. Proper development of the adductor group prevents soreness after participation in these sports.

Muscle identification

In developing a thorough and practical knowledge of the muscular system, it is essential that individual muscles be understood. Figs. 6-20 and 6-21 illustrate groups of muscles that work together to produce joint movement.

FIG. 6-19 • Gracilis muscle.

Modified from Anthony CP and Kolthoff NJ: Textbook of anatomy and physiology, ed. 9, St. Louis, The CV Mosby Co.

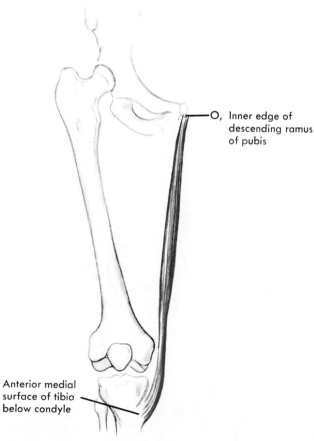

O, Inner edge of descending ramus of pubis

Anterior medial surface of tibia below condyle

FIG. 6-20 • **Left,** superficial muscles of the right upper leg, anterior surface. **Right,** superficial muscles of the right upper leg, posterior surface.

Modified from Anthony CP and Kolthoff NJ: Textbook of anatomy and physiology, ed. 9, St. Louis, The CV Mosby Co.

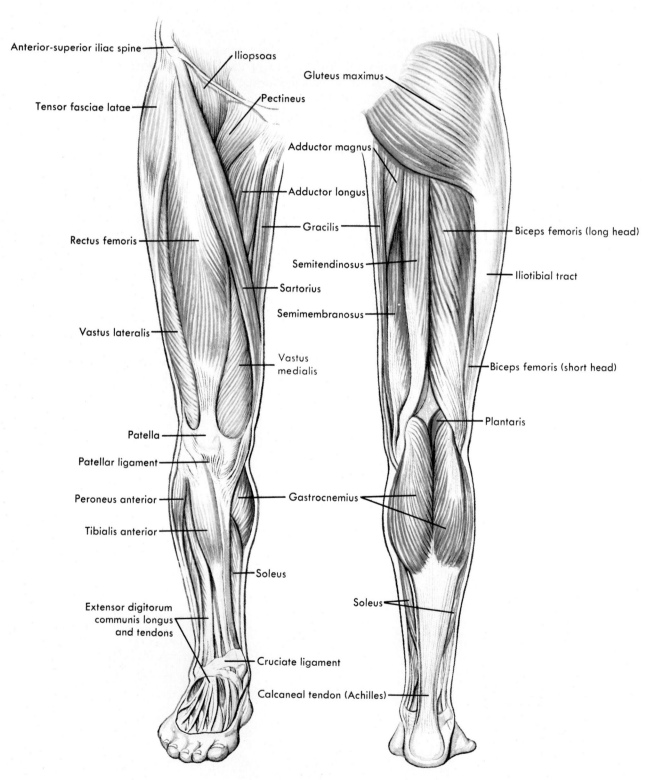

FIG. 6-21 • Cross-section of thigh at midsection.

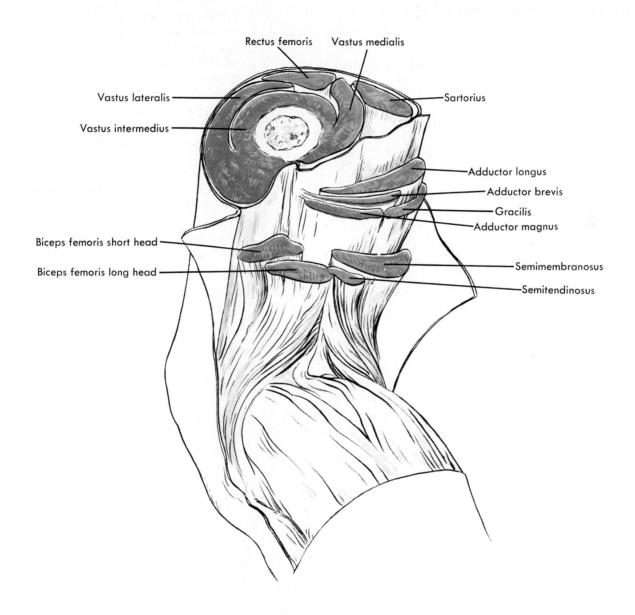

Laboratory and review exercises

As an aid to student learning and for assignments, in-class, out of class, or for teacher testing, tear-out worksheets are found at the end of the text (pages 171-172).

Additional laboratory and review exercises

1. Locate the following parts of the pelvic girdle and hip joint on a human skeleton and on a subject:
   a. *Skeleton*
      (1) Ilium
      (2) Ischium
      (3) Pubis
      (4) Symphysis pubis
      (5) Acetabulum
      (6) Rami (ascending and descending)
      (7) Obturator foramen
      (8) Ischial tuberosity
      (9) Anterior-superior iliac spine
   b. *Subject*
      (1) Crest of ilium
      (2) Anterior-superior iliac spine

2. How and where do you palpate the following muscles on a human subject?
   a. Gracilis
   b. Sartorius
   c. Gluteus maximus
   d. Gluteus medius
   e. Gluteus minimus
   f. Biceps femoris
   g. Rectus temoris
   h. Semimembranosus
   i. Semitendinosus
   j. Adductor magnus
   k. Adductor longus
   l. Adductor brevis

3. Be prepared to indicate on a human skeleton, using a long rubber band, where each muscle has its origin and insertion.

4. Distinguish between hip flexion and trunk flexion.

5. Demonstrate the movement and list the muscles primarily responsible for the following movements:
   a. Hip flexion
   b. Hip extension
   c. Hip adduction
   d. Hip abduction

6. How is walking different from running in relation to the use of the hip joint muscle actions?

7. Prepare an oral or written report on the ligaments of the pelvic girdle.

8. The hip joint and pelvic girdle muscles are listed at the left of the chart on p. 81. Place a check in the column for each action of the muscle. Add a "P" for primary action.

Muscle analysis chart • Hip joint and pelvic girdle

Muscles	Flexion	Extension	Abduction	Adduction	Outward Rotation	
Gluteus maximus						
Gluteus medius						
Gluteus minimus						
Biceps femoris						
Semimembranosus						
Semitendinosus						
Adductor magnus						
Adductor longus						
Adductor brevis						
Gracilis						
Outward rotators						
Rectus femoris						
Sartorius						
Pectinous						
Iliopsoas						
Tensor fascia lata						

References

Lysholm J and Wikland J: Injuries in runners, American Journal of Sports Medicine 15:168, September-October, 1986.

Noahes TD, et al: Pelvic stress fractures in long distance runners, American Journal of Sports Medicine 13:120, March-April, 1985.

Perreira J: Treating the quadriceps contusion, Scholastic Coach 57:38, October 1987.

The knee joint

Student objectives

• To explain the cartilageous and ligamentous structures of the knee joint.

• To draw and label on a skeletal chart muscles of the knee joint.

• To palpate the knee joint muscles on a human subject.

• To demonstrate with a fellow student the movements of the knee joint.

• To name and explain the actions and importance of the quadriceps and hamstring muscles.

• To list and organize the muscles that produce the movements of the knee joint.

The knee joint is the largest joint in the body and a complex joint. It is primarily a hinge joint. The combined functions of weight bearing and locomotion place considerable stress and strain on the knee joint. Powerful knee joint extensor and flexor muscles, combined with a strong ligamentous structure, provide a strong functioning joint in most instances.

In most physical activities, a strong and effective functioning knee joint is essential. To ensure a better understanding of the knee, a brief consideration of the ligaments and cartilage is presented.

Bones

The enlarged femoral condyles articulate on the enlarged surface of the tibia, somewhat in a horizontal line. Since the femur projects downward at an oblique angle, its medial condyle is slightly longer. The tibia bears all the weight, since the fibula has no connection with the femur. Fundamentally, the knee joint is a hinge joint, but there is a slight amount of rotation in certain positions.

The other bone of the knee joint is the patella, a sesamoid (floating) bone implanted in the quadriceps tendon and in the patellar ligament. Its location helps provide a better angle of pull and thus greater strength for the quadriceps muscles.

Cartilage and ligaments FIG. 7-1

Ligaments and muscle tendons help provide a solid support for the knee joint. Cartilage forms the cushion between the bones (Fig. 7-1). The surfaces between the femur and tibia are protected by cartilage formation attached to the tibia, which deepens the tibial fossa and acts as a cushion between the bones. There are two divisions of this protective cartilage.

The medial semilunar cartilage, or more technically, the medial meniscus, is located between the medial aspects of the femur and the tibia (Fig. 7-1). On the outside, the lateral semilunar cartilage (lateral meniscus) forms the protective layer. Both of these cartilages are thicker on the outside and taper down to membranous thickness. They can slip about slightly and are held in place by ligaments.

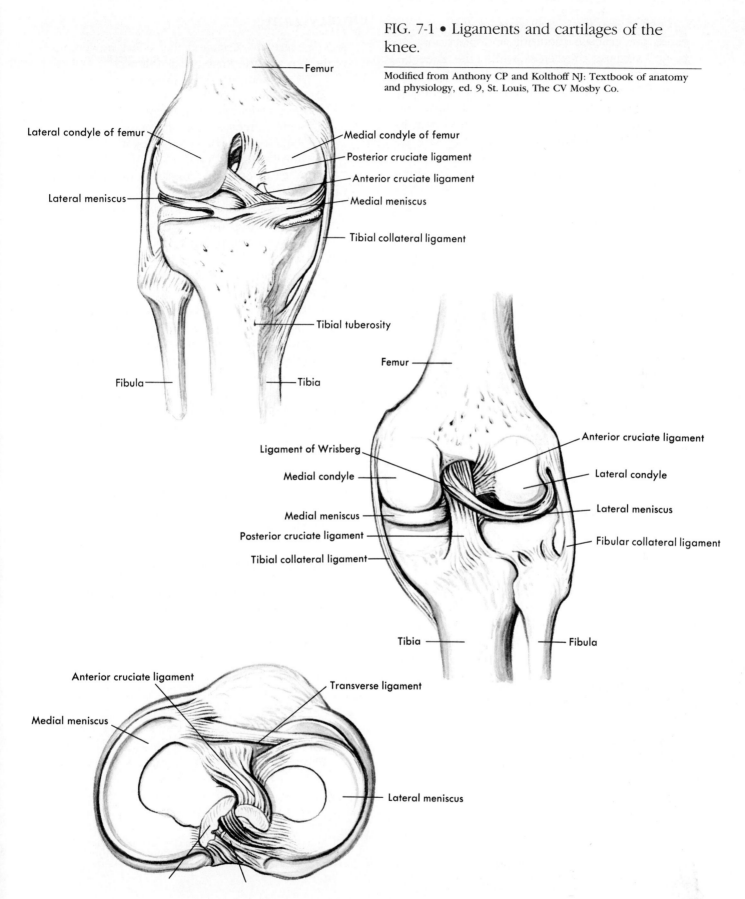

FIG. 7-1 • Ligaments and cartilages of the knee.

Modified from Anthony CP and Kolthoff NJ: Textbook of anatomy and physiology, ed. 9, St. Louis, The CV Mosby Co.

Femur

Lateral condyle of femur

Medial condyle of femur

Posterior cruciate ligament

Anterior cruciate ligament

Lateral meniscus

Medial meniscus

Tibial collateral ligament

Tibial tuberosity

Fibula

Tibia

Femur

Ligament of Wrisberg

Medial condyle

Medial meniscus

Posterior cruciate ligament

Tibial collateral ligament

Anterior cruciate ligament

Lateral condyle

Lateral meniscus

Fibular collateral ligament

Tibia

Fibula

Anterior cruciate ligament

Medial meniscus

Transverse ligament

Lateral meniscus

Other important ligaments of the knee include the cruciate (anterior and posterior), so named because they cross within the knee between the tibia and the femur. These ligaments maintain the inner stability of the knee joint (Fig. 7-1). Some authorities believe these ligaments can be stretched and the knee weakened by activities such as deep knee-bends and duck-walk exercises.

On the medial side of the knee is found the medial (tibial) collateral ligament (Fig. 7-1), which is attached to the medial meniscus. Blows to the knee from the outside stretch the medial ligament and sometimes pull or tear the cartilage, resulting in what is commonly called a "cartilage" of the knee.

Injury to the cartilage of the knee generally occurs when a blow is received from the outside (lateral side) of the knee. Stumbling down a stairs and twisting the knee or receiving a block in football from the outside can force the medial collateral ligament to stretch and in some cases to pull loose or tear the medial meniscus to which it is attached. An injury to the cartilage can be minor or very severe.

On the fibular (outside) side of the knee, the fibular (lateral) collateral ligament joins the fibula and the femur. Injuries to this ligament are infrequent.

Other ligaments of lesser importance are located in the knee.*

The knee joint is well supplied with synovial fluid from a synovial cavity, which lies under the patella and between the surfaces of the tibia and the femur. Commonly, this synovial cavity is called the "capsule of the knee." More than 10 bursae are located in the knee, some of which are connected to the synovial cavity. Bursae are located where they can absorb shock or prevent friction.

Movements

Flexion or bending at the knee.
Extension or straightening at the knee.
Rotation inward and outward.

---

*More detailed discussion of the knee is found in anatomy texts and training manuals.

Observation

Muscles already discussed that effect movement of the hip and the knee are as follows:

1. Rectus femoris—knee extensor
2. Sartorius—knee flexor
3. Biceps femoris—knee flexor
4. Semitendinosus—knee flexor
5. Semimembranosus—knee flexor
6. Gracilis—knee flexor

The gastrocnemius muscle, discussed in Chapter 8, is also a knee flexor.

Two-joint muscles are most effective when either origin or insertion is fixed by the contraction of muscles that will prevent movement in the direction of the pull.

As an example, the sartorius muscle becomes a better flexor at the knee when the pelvis is drawn up in front by the abdominal muscles, thus fixing the pelvis upward. This is exemplified by trying to flex the knee and cross the legs in the sitting position. One usually leans backward to flex the legs at the knees. Again, this is illustrated by kicking a football. The kicker invariably leans well backward to raise and fix the origin of the rectus femoris muscle to make it more effective as an extensor of the leg at the knee. Also, when youngsters hang by the knees, they flex the hips to fix or raise the origin of the hamstrings to make the latter more effective flexors of the knees.

Flexion and extension are the main movements at the knee, but it is possible to have some rotation at this joint. When the knee is flexed, some rotation either inward or outward can occur. The biceps femoris is responsible for outward rotation, while the semitendinosus and semimembraneous mainly produce inward rotation assisted by the sartorius, gracilis, and popliteus.

Quadriceps muscles

The ability to jump is essential in nearly all sports. Individuals who have good jumping ability always have strong quadriceps muscles that extend the leg at the knee. They are the rectus femoris (the only two-joint muscle of the group), vastus lateralis (the largest muscle of the group), vastus intermedius, and vastus medialis. All attach to the patella and by the patellar tendon to the tuberosity of the tibia. All are superficial and palpable except the vastus intermedius, which is under the rectus femoris. The vastus medialis extends most forcibly in the last 10 to 20 degrees of extension. In rehabilitation of knee injuries, athletic trainers always insist on complete extension of the joint. The vertical jump is a simple test that indicates the strength of the quadriceps. This muscle group is generally twice as strong as the hamstring muscle group (knee flexors).

Rectus femoris muscle SEE FIG. 6-6

Origin

Anterior-inferior spine of the ilium.

Insertion

Top of the patella and patellar ligament to the tibial tuberosity.

Action

Flexion of the hip.
Extension at the knee.

Palpation

Any place on the anterior surface of the femur.

Observation and exercise

See rectus femoris, Chapter 6, p 64 and above.

Vastus lateralis (externus) muscle

FIG. 7-2

Origin

Outer surface of the femur below the greater trochanter and upper half of the linea aspera.

Insertion

Outer half of the upper border of the patella and patellar ligament to the tibial tuberosity.

Action

Extension of the knee.

Palpation

Lateral middle side of the thigh.

Observation and exercise

See previous discussion this page.

Vastus intermedius muscle FIG. 7-3

Origin

Upper two thirds of the anterior surface of the femur.

Insertion

Upper border of the patella and patellar ligament to the tibial tuberosity.

Action

Extension of the knee.

Palpation

Cannot be palpated; under the rectus femoris muscle.

Observation and exercise

All three of the vastus muscles function with the rectus femoris in knee extension. They are used typically in walking and in running and must be used to keep the knees straight, as in standing. When the hip is flexed, the rectus femoris becomes less effective as an extensor of the knee. The work is then done primarily by the three vasti muscles.

The three vasti muscles all contract in extension at the knee. They are used together with the rectus femoris in running, jumping, hopping, skipping, and walking. The vasti are primarily responsible for extending the knee while the hip is flexed or being flexed. Thus in doing a knee bend with the trunk bent forward at the hip, the vasti are exercised with little involvement of the rectus femoris. The natural activities mentioned develop the quadriceps. Knee bends with a barbell of varying weights on the shoulders, depending on strength, are an excellent exercise. Leg-press exercises with weight machine apparatus using heavy weights is another good exercise.

FIG. 7-2 • Vastus lateralis muscle.

Modified from Anthony CP and Kolthoff NJ: Textbook of anatomy and physiology, ed. 9, St. Louis, The CV Mosby Co.

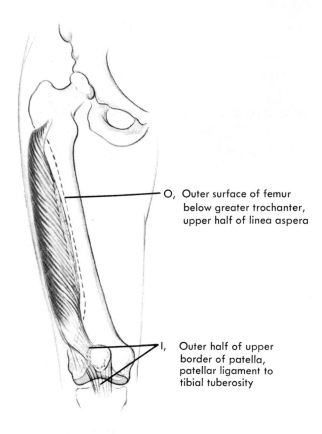

O, Outer surface of femur
below greater trochanter,
upper half of linea aspera

I, Outer half of upper
border of patella,
patellar ligament to
tibial tuberosity

FIG. 7-3 • Vastus intermedius muscle.

Modified from Anthony CP and Kolthoff NJ: Textbook of anatomy and physiology, ed. 9, St. Louis, The CV Mosby Co.

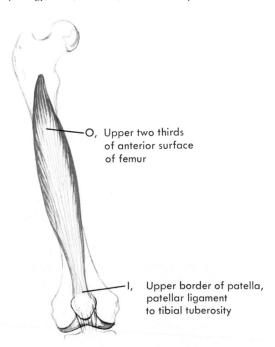

O, Upper two thirds
of anterior surface
of femur

I, Upper border of patella,
patellar ligament
to tibial tuberosity

Vastus medialis (internus) muscle FIG. 7-4

Origin

Whole length of the linea aspera and the internal condyloid ridge.

Insertion

Inner half of the upper border of the patella and patellar ligament to the tibial tuberosity.

Action

Extension of the knee.

Palpation

Anterior-medial side of the thigh near the knee joint.

Observation and exercise

See p. 85.

Hamstring muscles

Injuries to hamstring muscles are very common in football and other sports. The hamstring muscles are antagonists to the quadriceps muscles at the knee and are named for their cordlike attachments at the knee. They include the biceps femoris, semitendinosus, and semimembranosus muscles. All the hamstrings originate on the ischial tuberosity of the pelvic bone, and the semitendinosus and semimembranosus insert on the medial side of the tibia. The biceps femoris inserts on the lateral tibial condyle and head of the fibula—hence the saying, "Two to the inside and one to the outside." The second head of the biceps femoris is on the linea aspera of the femur. Special exercises to improve the strength of this muscle group are factors in decreasing knee injuries.

Hamstrings are primarily knee flexors and secondarily hip extensors. Inability to touch the floor with the fingers when the knees are straight is largely a result of a lack of flexibility of the hamstrings.

Rotation of the knee can occur when it is in a flexed position. Knee rotation is brought about by the hamstring muscles. The biceps femoris provides the force for outward rotation, and the semitendinosus and semimembranosus cause the inward rotation. Rotation of the knee permits pivoting movements and change in direction of the body.

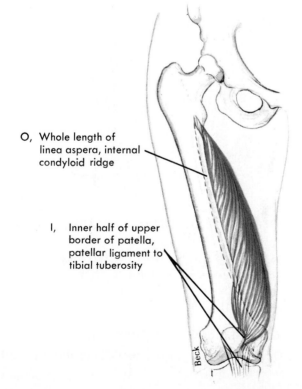

O, Whole length of linea aspera, internal condyloid ridge

I, Inner half of upper border of patella, patellar ligament to tibial tuberosity

Beck

FIG. 7-4 • Vastus medialis muscle.

Modified from Anthony CP and Kolthoff NJ: Textbook of anatomy and physiology, ed. 9, St. Louis, The CV Mosby Co.

Popliteus muscle FIG. 7-5

Origin

Posterior surface of the outer condyle of the femur.

Insertion

Upper posterior-medial surface of the tibia.

Action

Flexion of the knee.

Palpation

Cannot be palpated.

Observation and exercise

The popliteus muscle is the only typical flexor of the leg at the knee. All other flexors are two-joint muscles. It acts with cruciate ligaments to prevent the leg from bending backward.

Hanging from a bar with the legs flexed at the knee strenuously exercises the popliteus muscle. Also, the less strenuous activities of walking and running exercise this muscle.

Muscle identification

In Fig. 7-6, identify the muscles of the anterior thigh and knee areas.

FIG. 7-5 • Popliteus muscle.

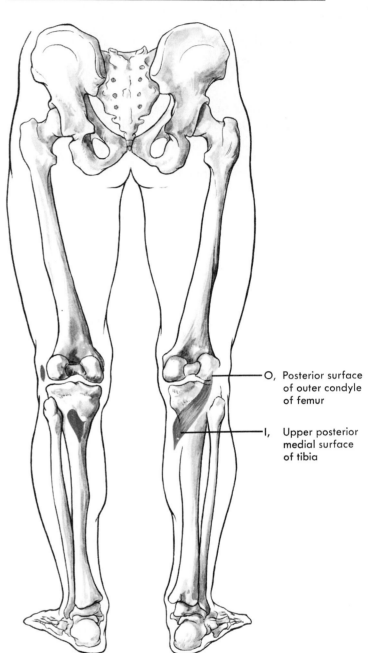

O, Posterior surface of outer condyle of femur

I, Upper posterior medial surface of tibia

Laboratory and review exercises

As an aid to student learning and for assignments; in-class, out-of-class or for teacher testing, a tear-out worksheet is found at the end of the text (page 173).

Posterior skeletal worksheet (no. 1)

Draw and label on the worksheet the knee joint muscles.

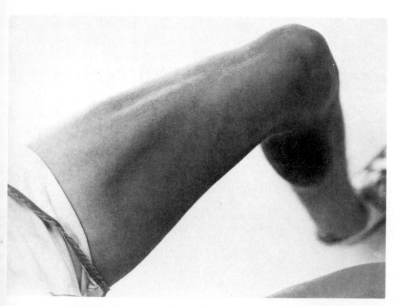

FIG. 7-6 • Muscles of the anterior thigh and knee.

Additional laboratory and review exercises

1. Locate the following parts of bones on a human skeleton and on a subject:
   a. *Skeleton*
      (1) Head and neck of femur
      (2) Greater trochanter
      (3) Shaft of femur
      (4) Lesser trochanter
      (5) Linea aspera
      (6) Adductor tubercle
      (7) Medial epicondyle
      (8) Lateral epicondyle
      (9) Patella
   b. *Subject*
      (1) Greater trochanter
      (2) Adductor tubercle
      (3) Medial epicondyle
      (4) Lateral epicondyle
      (5) Patella
2. How and where do you palpate the following muscles on a human subject? NOTE: Palpate the previously studied hip two joint muscles while they are performing actions at the knee.

   a. Gracilis   f. Rectus femoris
   b. Sartorius   g. Vastus lateralis
   c. Biceps femoris   h. Vastus intermedius
   d. Semitendinosus   i. Vastus medialis
   e. Semimembranosus   j. Popliteus

3. Be prepared to indicate on a human skeleton, by a long rubber band, the origin and insertion of the muscles just listed.
4. Demonstrate the movements and list the muscles primarily responsible for the following movements:
   a. Extension of leg at knee
   b. Flexion of leg at knee
5. Discuss or have reports from authorities on the acceptability of deep knee-bends and duck-walk activities in a physical education program.
6. Prepare a special report on the knee, including its ligamentous structure, joint structure, functioning, common injuries, and taping for injuries.
7. Discuss or have reports on preventive and corrective exercises to strengthen the knee joint.
8. In the chart below list the muscles primarily responsible for knee joint movement.

Muscle analysis chart • Knee joint

Knee joint	
Flexion	Extension
Inward rotation	Outward rotation

References

Baker BE, et al: Review of meniscal injury and associated sports, American Journal of Sports Medicine 13:1, January-February 1985.

Evans W: Hamstring strength and flexibility development, Scholastic Coach 56:42, April 1987.

Garrick JG and Regna RK: Prophyactic knee bracing, American Journal of Sports Medicine 15:471, September-October 1987.

Hemba G: Strength development below the knee, Athletic Journal 66:24, September 1985.

Kelly DW, et al: Patellar and quadriceps tendon ruptures—jumping knee, American Journal of Sports Medicine 12:375, September-October 1984.

Kroll W, et al: Isometric knee extension and plantar flexion: muscle fatigue and fiber type composition in female distance runners, Research Quarterly for Exercise and Sports 52:200, May 1981.

Lysholm J and Wikland J: Injuries in runners, American Journal of Sports Medicine 15:168, September-October 1986.

Perreira J: Treating the quadriceps contusion, Scholastic Coach 57:38, October 1987.

Wroble RR, et al: Pattern of knee injuries in wrestling, a six-year study, American Journal of Sports Medicine 14:55, January-February 1986.

The ankle and foot

8

Student objectives

• To identify on the human skeleton the bones, ligaments, and arches of the ankle and foot.

• To draw and label on a skeletal chart the muscles of the ankle and foot.

• To palpate on a human subject the muscles of the ankle and foot.

• To list and organize the muscles that produce the movements of the ankle and foot.

The complexity of the foot is evidenced by the 26 bones, 19 large muscles, many small (intrinsic) muscles, and more than 100 ligaments that make up the structure of the foot.

Support and propulsion are the two functions of the foot. Proper functioning and adequate development of the muscles of the foot and practice of good foot mechanics are essential for everyone. In our modern society, foot trouble is one of the most common ailments. Poor foot mechanics begun early in life will inevitably lead to foot discomfort in later years.

The fitness revolution that has occurred in the past two decades has resulted in great improvements in shoes available for sports and recreational activities. In the past, a pair of sneakers would suffice for most activities. Now there are basketball, baseball, football, jogging, soccer, tennis, and walking shoes. Good shoes are important, but there is no substitute for adequate muscular development, strength, and good foot mechanics.

Bones

Each foot has 26 bones that are shaped in the form of an arch. They connect with the upper body bony structure through the fibula and tibia (Figs. 8-1 and 8-2). Body weight is transferred from the tibia to the talus and the calcaneus.

FIG. 8-1 • Right fibula and tibia.

From Anthony CP and Kolthoff NJ: Textbook of anatomy and physiology, ed. 9, St. Louis, The CV Mosby Co.

FIG. 8-2 • Right foot.

Modified from Anthony CP and Kolthoff NJ: Textbook of anatomy and physiology, ed. 9, St. Louis, The CV Mosby Co.

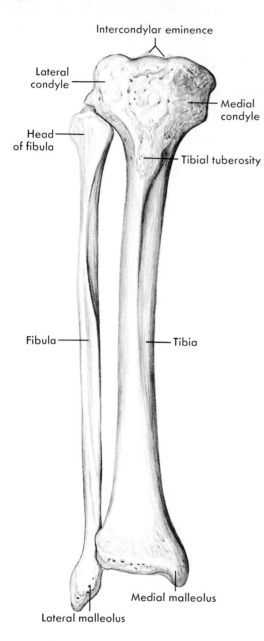

Intercondylar eminence

Lateral condyle

Medial condyle

Head of fibula

Tibial tuberosity

Fibula

Tibia

Medial malleolus

Lateral malleolus

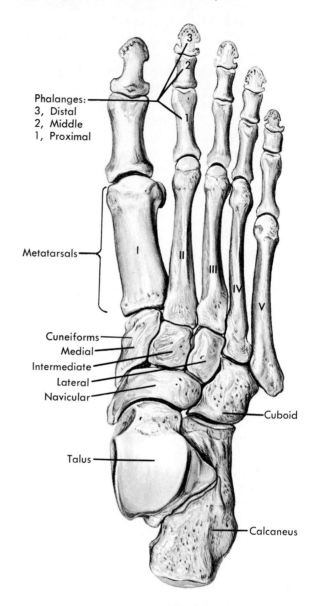

Phalanges:
3, Distal
2, Middle
1, Proximal

Metatarsals

Cuneiforms
Medial
Intermediate
Lateral
Navicular

Cuboid

Talus

Calcaneus

91

Ligaments

Ligaments in the foot and the ankle have the difficult task of maintaining the position of an arch. All 26 bones in the foot are connected with ligaments. This brief discussion is focused on large ligaments that make up the longitudinal and transverse arches.

The longitudinal arch (ligaments) can be described as a long arch and a short arch (Fig. 8-3). The long arch is located on the medial side of the foot and extends from the calcaneus bone to the talus, the navicular, the three cuneiforms, and the proximal ends of the three medial metatarsals. The short arch is located on the lateral side of the foot and extends from the calcaneus to the cuboid and proximal ends of the fourth and fifth metatarsals. Individual long arches vary from high, medium, and low, but a low arch is not necessarily a weak arch.

The transverse arch (Fig. 8-3) extends across the foot from one metatarsal bone to the other.

Movements

Dorsal flexion—movement of the top of the ankle and foot toward the anterior tibia bone; accomplished by the extensor muscles of the ankle.

Plantar flexion—movement of the ankle and foot downward; accomplished by the flexor muscles of the ankle.

Eversion (pronation)—turning the ankle and foot outward; weight on the medial edge of the foot.

Inversion (supination)—turning the ankle and foot inward; weight on the lateral edge of the foot.

Toe flexion—movement of the toes toward the floor.

Toe extension—movement of the toes upward.

Ankle and foot muscles

The large number of muscles in the ankle and foot may pose some problems for the beginning student. In general the muscles located on the anterior of the ankle and foot are the dorsal flexors. Those to the posterior are plantar flexors. Muscles that are pronators (eversion) are located more to the lateral side, while supinators (inversion) are more to the medial side.

Plantar flexors
  Gastrocnemius
  Flexor digitorum longus
  Flexor hallucis longus
  Peroneus longus
  Peroneus brevis
  Plantaris
  Soleus
  Tibialis posterior

Evertors-Pronators
  Peroneus longus
  Peroneus brevis
  Extensor digitorum longus

Dorsal flexors
  Tibialis anterior
  Extensor digitorum longus
  Extensor hallucis longus

Invertors-Supinators
  Tibialis anterior
  Tibialis posterior
  Flexor digitorum longus
  Flexor hallucis longus

NOTE: A number of the ankle and foot muscles are capable of helping produce more than one movement.

FIG. 8-3 • Longitudinal and transverse arches.

Modified from Anthony CP and Kolthoff NJ: Textbook of anatomy and physiology, ed. 9, St. Louis, The CV Mosby Co.

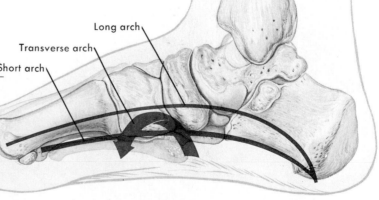

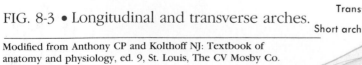

Gastrocnemius muscle FIG. 8-4

Origin

Posterior surfaces of the two condyles of the femur.

Insertion

Posterior surface of the calcaneus (Archilles tendon).

Action

Plantar flexion of the ankle.
Flexion at the knee.

Palpation

Easiest muscle in the lower extremity to palpate; upper posterior aspect of the lower leg.

Observation

The gastrocnemius muscle is more effective as a knee flexor if the foot is elevated and more effective as a plantar flexor of the foot if the knee is held in extension. This is observed when one sits too close to the wheel in driving a car. When the knees are bent, the muscle becomes an ineffective plantar flexor, and it is more difficult to depress the brakes. This is also obvious in sprint races. At the start of a race, the signal "get set" allows the sprinter to lean well forward and approximately straighten the starting knee, which in turn makes the gastrocnemius more effective in plantar flexing the ankle and foot and driving the body forward.

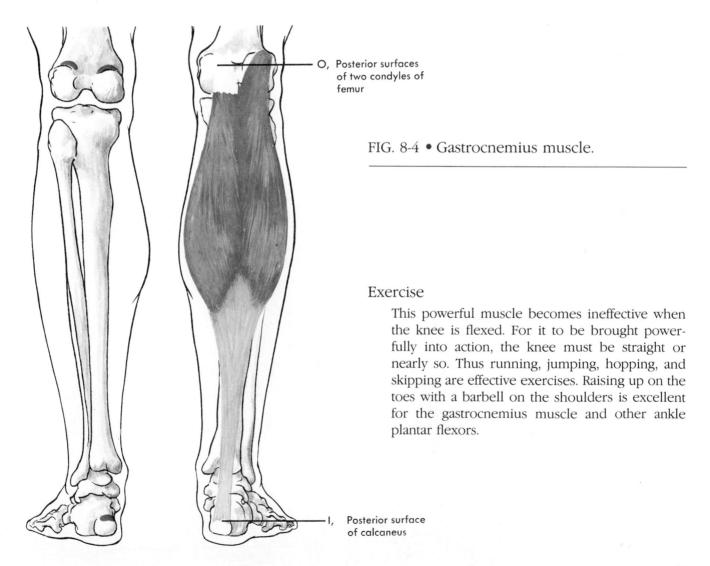

O, Posterior surfaces of two condyles of femur

I, Posterior surface of calcaneus

FIG. 8-4 • Gastrocnemius muscle.

Exercise

This powerful muscle becomes ineffective when the knee is flexed. For it to be brought powerfully into action, the knee must be straight or nearly so. Thus running, jumping, hopping, and skipping are effective exercises. Raising up on the toes with a barbell on the shoulders is excellent for the gastrocnemius muscle and other ankle plantar flexors.

Soleus muscle FIG. 8-5

Origin

Upper two thirds of the posterior surfaces of the tibia and fibula.

Insertion

Posterior surface of the calcaneus (Achilles tendon).

Action

Plantar flexion of the ankle.

Palpation

Under the gastrocnemius muscle on the lateral side of the lower leg.

Observation and exercise

The soleus muscle is one of the most important muscles used in producing plantar flexion of the ankle. Some anatomists believe that it is nearly as important in this movement as the gastrocnemius. This is especially true when the knee is flexed. When an individual rises up on his toes, the soleus muscle can plainly be seen on the outside of the lower leg if one has exercised the legs extensively as in running and walking.

The soleus muscle is used whenever the ankle is plantar flexed. Any movement with body weight on the foot or the knee flexed or extended calls it into action. Running, jumping, hopping, skipping, and dancing on the toes are valuable exercises for the soleus.

FIG. 8-5 • Soleus muscle.

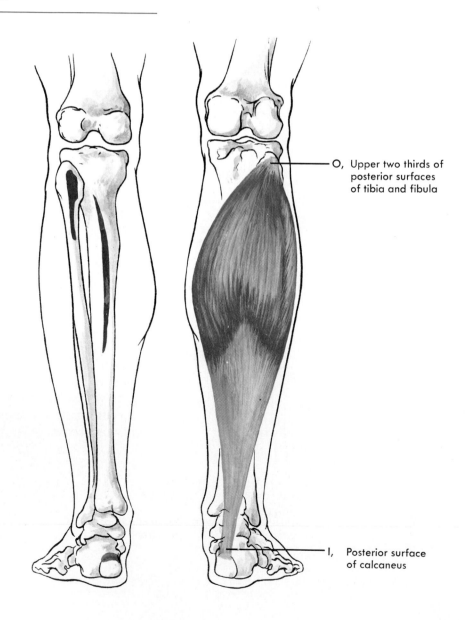

O, Upper two thirds of posterior surfaces of tibia and fibula

I, Posterior surface of calcaneus

94

Tibialis posterior muscle FIG. 8-6

Origin

Posterior surface of the upper half of the inter-osseus membrane and adjacent surfaces of the tibia and fibula.

Insertion

Lower inner surfaces of the navicular and cunei-form bones and bases of the second, third, fourth, and fifth metatarsal bones.

Action

Plantar flexion of the ankle and inversion of the foot.

Palpation

Cannot be palpated.

Observation and exercise

Passing down the back of the leg, under the me-dial malleolus, then forward to the navicular and medial cuneiform bones, the tibialis posterior muscle pulls down from the underside and plan-tar flexes the foot. It is an important muscle in inversion of the ankle. "Shin splint" is a term fre-quently used to describe a condition in which the tibialis posterior, tibialis anterior, and extensor digitorum longus muscles are injured. Sprints and long distance running are common causes.

Use of the tibialis posterior muscle in plantar flexion and inversion gives support to the longi-tudinal arch of the foot. This muscle is generally used in the same movements prescribed for the soleus and gastrocnemius muscles.

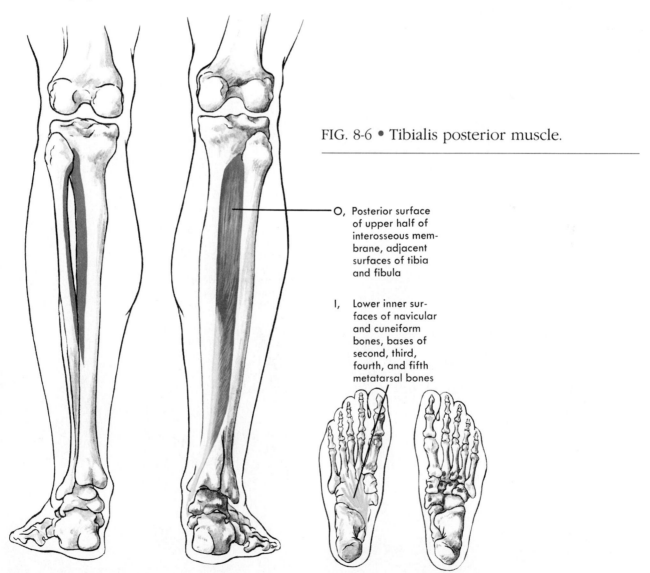

FIG. 8-6 • Tibialis posterior muscle.

O, Posterior surface of upper half of interosseous mem-brane, adjacent surfaces of tibia and fibula

I, Lower inner sur-faces of navicular and cuneiform bones, bases of second, third, fourth, and fifth metatarsal bones

Flexor digitorum longus muscle

FIG. 8-7

Origin

Lower two thirds of the posterior surface of the tibia.

Insertion

Base of the distal phalanx of each of the four outer toes.

Action

Plantar flexion of the ankle, flexion of the toes, and inversion of the foot.

Palpation

Cannot be palpated.

Observation and exercise

Passing down the back of the lower leg under the medial malleolus and then forward, the flexor digitorum longus muscle draws the toes down and back toward the heel as it plantar flexes the ankle. It thus becomes very important in maintaining the longitudinal arch because it tends to lift the arch when it contracts.

Walking, running, and jumping do not necessarily call the flexor digitorum longus muscle into action. Some of the weak foot and ankle conditions result from ineffective use of the flexor digitorum longus. Walking barefoot with the toes curled downward toward the heels and with the foot inverted will give this muscle excellent exercise.

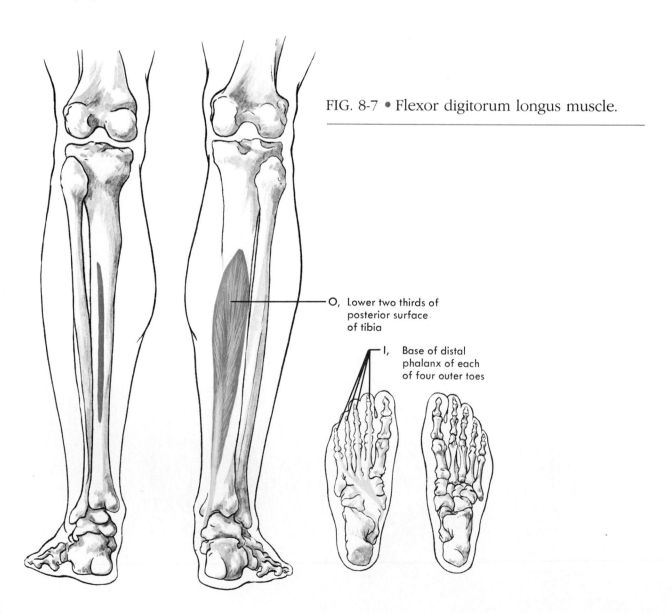

FIG. 8-7 • Flexor digitorum longus muscle.

O, Lower two thirds of posterior surface of tibia

I, Base of distal phalanx of each of four outer toes

Flexor hallucis longus muscle FIG. 8-8

Origin

Lower two thirds of the posterior surface of the fibula.

Insertion

Base of the distal phalanx of the big toe, undersurface.

Action

Plantar flexion of the big toe.
Plantar flexion of the ankle and inversion of the foot.

Palpation

Inside the calcaneal tendon near the heel.

Observation and exercise

Pulling from the underside of the great toe, the flexor hallucis longus muscle may work independently of the flexor digitorum longus muscle or with it. These two muscles, in a poorly developed condition, cramp easily when they are called on to do activities to which they are unaccustomed. These muscles are used effectively in walking if the toes are used (as they should be) in maintaining balance as each step is taken. Walking "with" the toes rather than "over" them is important action for them.

When the gastrocnemius, soleus, tibialis posterior, peroneus longus, peroneus brevis, flexor digitorum longus, flexor digitorum brevis, and flexor hallucis longus muscles are all used effectively in walking, the strength of the ankle is evident. A weak ankle and foot means, in most cases, lack of use of all the muscles just mentioned. Running, walking, jumping, hopping, and skipping will provide sufficient exercise for this muscle group. Good musculature in the foot is necessary to help prevent foot weakness.

FIG. 8-8 • Flexor hallucis longus muscle.

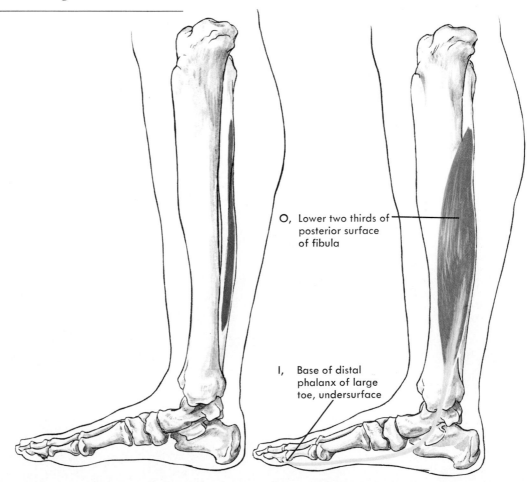

O, Lower two thirds of posterior surface of fibula

I, Base of distal phalanx of large toe, undersurface

Peroneus longus muscle FIG. 8-9

Origin

Head and upper two thirds of the outer surface of the fibula.

Insertion

Undersurfaces of the medial cuneiform and first metatarsal bones.

Action

Plantar flexion of the ankle and eversion of the foot.

Palpation

Third muscle on the lateral side of the tibia; upper lateral side of the tibia.

Observation and exercise

The peroneus longus muscle passes to the rear and under the lateral malleolus and under the foot from the outside to the under inner surface, thus plantar flexing the foot and at the same time pulling across the foot, aiding in preservation of the metatarsal arch.

When the peroneus longus muscle is used effectively with the other ankle flexors, it helps bind the transverse arch as it flexes. Developed without the other plantar flexors, it would produce a weak, everted foot. In running, jumping, hopping, and skipping, the foot should be placed so that it is pointing forward to give proper development of the group. Walking barefoot or in stocking feet on the inside of the foot (everted position) is the best exercise for this muscle.

FIG. 8-9 • Peroneus longus muscle.

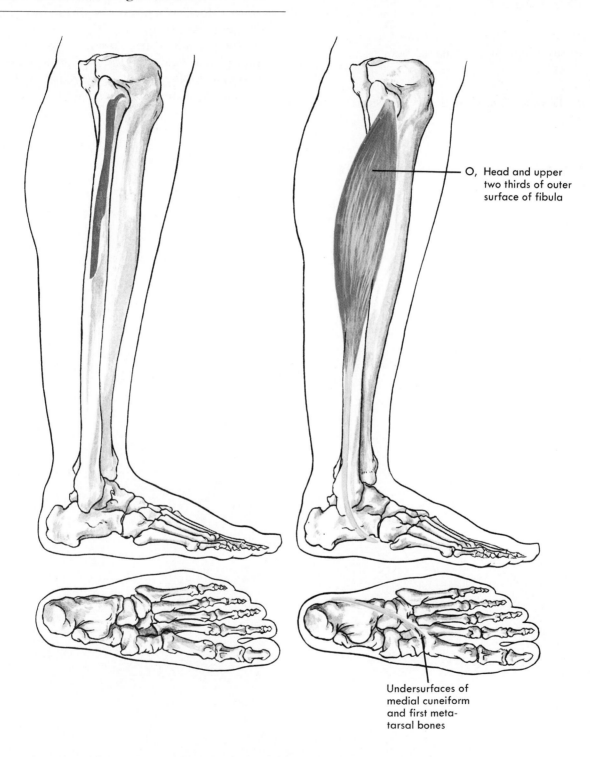

O, Head and upper
two thirds of outer
surface of fibula

Undersurfaces of
medial cuneiform
and first meta-
tarsal bones

Peroneus brevis and tertius muscles FIG. 8-10

Origin

Lower two thirds and lower third of the outer surface of the fibula.

Insertion

Tuberosity of the fifth metatarsal bone.

Action

Plantar flexion of the ankle and eversion of the foot.

Palpation

Tendon of the muscle at the proximal end of the fifth metatarsal.

Observation and exercise

The peroneus brevis muscle passes down behind and under the lateral malleolus to pull on the base of the fifth metatarsal. This muscle aids in maintaining the longitudinal arch as it depresses the foot. It is also an evertor of the foot proper. The peroneus tertius can act in dorsal flexion.

The peroneus brevis muscle is exercised with other plantar flexors in the power movements of running, jumping, hopping, and skipping. Everted foot walking is the best exercise for this muscle.

FIG. 8-10 • Peroneus brevis muscle.

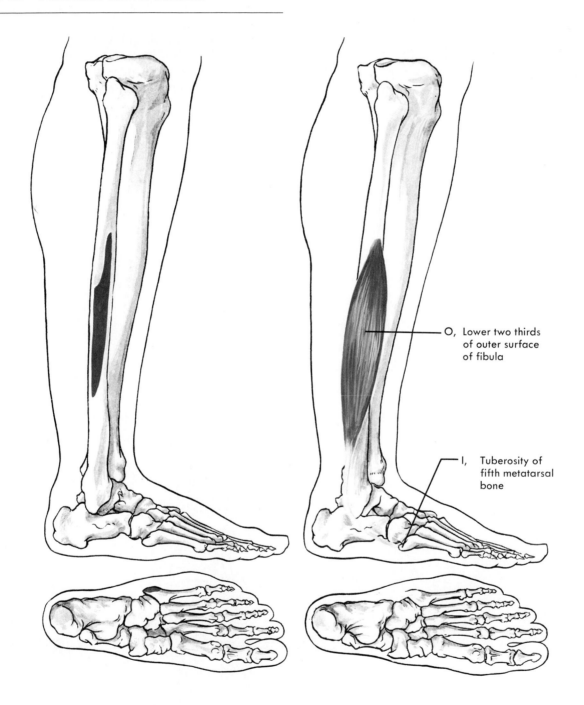

O, Lower two thirds
of outer surface
of fibula

I, Tuberosity of
fifth metatarsal
bone

Tibialis anterior muscle FIG. 8-11

Origin

Upper two thirds of the outer surface of the tibia.

Insertion

Inner surface of the medial cuneiform and the first metatarsal bone.

Action

Dorsal flexion of the ankle and inversion of the foot.

Palpation

First muscle to the lateral side of the tibia.

Observation and exercise

By its insertion, the tibialis anterior muscle is in a fine position to hold up the inner margin of the foot. However, as it contracts, it dorsal flexes the ankle and is used as an antagonist to the plantar flexors of the ankle. The tibialis anterior is forced to contract strongly when a person ice skates or walks on the outside of the foot. It strongly supports the long arch in inversion.

Walking barefoot or in stocking feet on the outside of the foot (inversion) is an excellent exercise for the tibialis anterior muscle.

FIG. 8-11 • Tibialis anterior muscle.

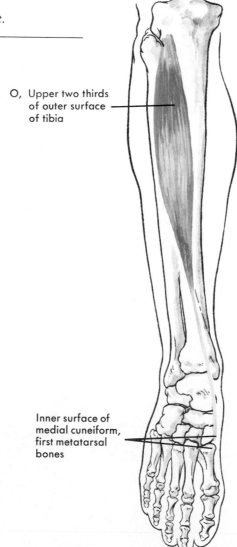

O, Upper two thirds of outer surface of tibia

Inner surface of medial cuneiform, first metatarsal bones

Extensor digitorum longus muscle FIG. 8-12

Origin

Outer condyle of the tibia, head of the fibula, and upper two thirds of the anterior surface of the fibula.

Insertion

Tops of the middle and distal phalanges of the four outer toes.

Action

Dorsal flexion of the ankle and eversion of the foot; extension of toes 2 to 5.

Palpation

Second muscle on the lateral side of the tibia; upper lateral side of the tibia.

Observation and exercise

Strength is necessary in the extensor digitorum longus muscle to maintain balance between the plantar and the dorsal flexors.

Action that involves dorsi flexion of the foot and toes against the resistance of the foot and toe flexion strengthens both the extensor digitorum longus and the extensor hallucis longus muscles.

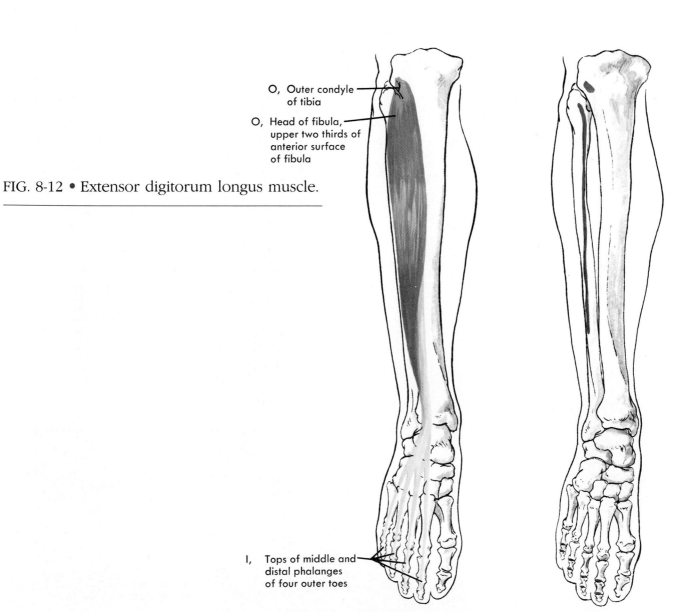

O, Outer condyle of tibia

O, Head of fibula, upper two thirds of anterior surface of fibula

I, Tops of middle and distal phalanges of four outer toes

FIG. 8-12 • Extensor digitorum longus muscle.

Extensor hallucis longus muscle

FIG. 8-13

Origin

Middle two thirds of the inner surface of the front of the fibula.

Insertion

Top of the distal phalanx of the great toe.

Action

Dorsal flexion of the ankle, toe extension, and foot inversion.

Palpation

Near the great toe on the dorsal surface.

Observation and exercise

The three dorsi flexors of the foot—tibialis anterior, extensor digitorum longus, and extensor hallucis longus—may be exercised by attempting to walk on the heels with the ankle and toes flexed dorsally. They may be strenuously exercised by hanging from a horizontal bar by the tops of the toes. Keep hands on the bar, and take as much weight as possible with the toes.

The fitness emphasis of recent years, with a great increase in the number of joggers, runners, and walkers of all ages, will result in increased strength of this area and fewer foot problems.

FIG. 8-13 • Extensor hallucis longus muscle.

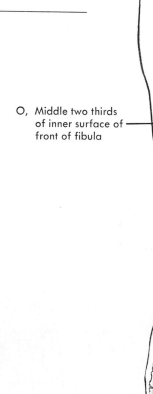
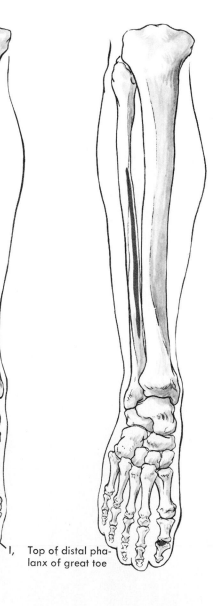

O, Middle two thirds of inner surface of front of fibula

I, Top of distal phalanx of great toe

104

Muscle identification

In developing a thorough and practical knowledge of the muscular system, it is essential that individual muscles be understood, as well as how groups of muscles work together to produce joint movement (Fig. 8-14).

Intrinsic muscles of the foot

Intrinsic muscles of the foot have their origin and insertion on the bones within the foot. Four layers of these muscles are found on the plantar surface of the foot. The following muscles are found in the four layers:

First layer—Adductor hallucis, flexor digitorum brevis, abductor digiti quinti

Second layer—Quadratus plantae, lumbricales (four)

Third layer—Flexor hallucis brevis, flexor digiti quinti brevis, adductor hallucis

Fourth layer—Interossei (seven)

Muscles are developed and maintain their strength only when they are used. One factor in the great increase in weak foot conditions is the lack of exercise to develop these muscles. Walking is one of the best activities for maintaining and developing these many small muscles that help support the arch of the foot.

Further discussion and consideration of the foot are beyond the scope of this book.

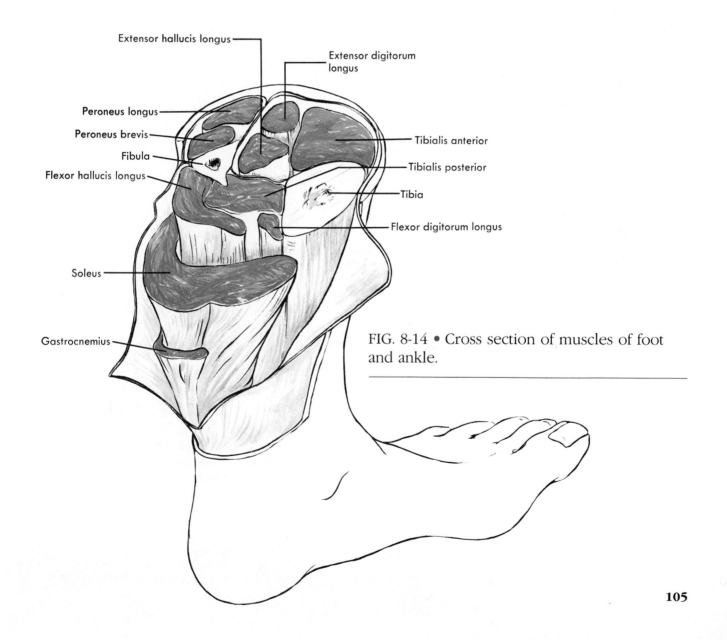

FIG. 8-14 • Cross section of muscles of foot and ankle.

Laboratory and review exercises

As an aid to student learning and for assignments, in-class, out-of-class or for teacher testing tear-out worksheets are found at the end of the text (page 175).

Anterior and posterior skeletal worksheet (no. 1)

Draw and label on the worksheet the following muscles of the ankle and foot.

a. Tibialis anterior
b. Extensor digitorum longus
c. Peroneus longus
d. Peroneus brevis
e. Soleus
f. Gastrocnemius
g. Extensor hallucis longus
h. Tibialis posterior
i. Flexor digitorum longus
j. Flexor hallucis longus

Additional laboratory and review exercises

1. Locate the following parts of the ankle and foot on a human skeleton and on a subject.
   a. Lateral malleolus
   b. Medial malleolus
   c. Calcaneus
   d. Navicular
   e. Three cuneiform bones
   f. Metatarsal bones
   g. Phalanges

2. How and where do you palpate the following muscles on a human subject?
   a. Tibialis anterior
   b. Extensor digitorum longus
   c. Peroneus longus
   d. Peroneus brevis
   e. Soleus
   f. Gastrocnemius
   g. Extensor hallucis longus
   h. Flexor digitorum longus
   i. Flexor hallucis longus
3. Demonstrate the following movements.
   a. Plantar flexion
   b. Dorsal flexion
   c. Inversion
   d. Eversion
4. Why are "low arches" and "flat feet" not synonymous terms?
5. Discuss the part that good foot mechanics plays in proper foot health.
6. What are orthotics?
7. Read and report on some common foot disorders: flat feet, ankle injuries, and orthopedic shoes.
8. Report orally or in writing on magazine articles that rate running and walking shoes.

References

Dearing M and Ziccardi NJ: Prevention and rehabilitation of ankle injuries, Athletic Journal 66:28, November 1985.

Coughlin LP, et al: Fracture dislocation of the tarsal navicular: a case report, American Journal of Sports Medicine 15:614, November-December 1987.

Franco AH: Pes cavus and pes planus—analysis and treatment, Physical Therapy 67:688, May 1987.

Grace P: Prevention and rehabilitation of shin splints, Scholastic Coach 57:47, March 1988.

Henderson J: Baring the soles, Runners World 22:14, November 1987.

Robinson M: Feet first, Coach and Athlete 44:30, August-September 1981.

Sammarcho GJ: Foot and ankle injuries in sports (symposium), American Journal of Sports Medicine, November-December 1987.

The trunk

9

Student objectives

• To identify and differentiate the different types of vertebrae in the spinal column.

• To label on a skeletal chart the types of vertebrae and important features.

• To draw and label on a skeletal chart some of the muscles of the trunk and the spinal column.

• To palpate on a human subject some of the muscles of the trunk and spinal column.

• To list and organize the muscles that produce the primary movements of the trunk and spinal column.

The trunk and thorax present problems in kinesiology that are not found in the study of other parts of the body. First is the complexity of the vertebral column. It consists of 24 intricate and complex vertebrae. These vertebrae contain the spinal column with its 31 pairs of spinal nerves. Unquestionably it is the most complex part of the human body other than the brain and the central nervous system.

The anterior portion of the trunk contains the abdominal muscles, which are different from other muscles in that they do not attach from bone to bone. In addition, the vertebral column contains many small intrinsic muscles, the consideration of which is far beyond the scope of this book.

Bones

Vertebral column FIGS. 9-1 and 9-2

The intricate and complex bony structure of the vertebral column consists of 24 vertebrae. The column is further divided into the cervical (neck) 7 vertebrae, thoracic (chest) 12 vertebrae, and lumbar (lower back) 5 vertebrae. The first two cervical vertebrae are unique in that their shapes allow for extensive movements of the head to the sides as well as forward and backward. The normal curves of the spine enables it to absorb blows and shocks.

Thorax

The skeletal foundation of the thorax is formed by 12 pairs of ribs. Seven pairs are true ribs in that they attach directly to the sternum. Five pairs are considered false ribs, three of which attach indirectly to the sternum; and two pairs of ribs are floating ribs in that their ends are free. The manubrium, the body of the sternum and the xiphoid process are the other bones of the thorax. All of the ribs are attached posteriorly to the vertebral column.

Movements

Flexion of the trunk—forward movement of the spine.

Extension of the trunk—return from flexion or backward movement of the spine.

Lateral flexion (left or right)—movement of the shoulder toward the hip on either side.

Rotation of the trunk—rotary movement of the spine in the horizontal plane.

Spinal column muscles

A few large muscles and numerous small muscles are found in this area. The largest muscle is the erector spinae (sacrospinalis), which extends on each side of the spinal column from the pelvic region to the cranium. It is divided into three muscles, spinalis, longissimus, and iliocostalis, from the medial to the lateral side it has attachments in the lumbar, thoracic, and cervical region. Thus the erector spinae can be said to be made up of nine muscles.

Numerous small muscles are found in the spinal column region. Many of them have their origin on one vertebra and insertion on the next vertebra. They are important muscles in the functioning of the spine, but the knowledge of these muscles is of limited value to most individuals who use this text.

Posterior muscles

Erector spinae (Sacrospinalis)
    Spinalis—dorsi, cervicis, capitis
    Longissimus—dorsi, cervicis, capitis
    Iliocostalis—lumborum, dorsi, cervicis
Splenius—capitis and cervicis
Quadratus lumborum
Rotatores—entire spinal column
Multifidus—entire spinal column
Suboccipital
Serratus—superior
Serratus—inferior
Interspinales—entire spinal column
Intertransversales—entire spinal column

Anterior muscles

Some of the anterior muscles are different from other muscles that have been studied. They do not go from bone to bone but attach into an aponeurosis (fascia) around the rectus abdominis area. They are the obliquus externus abdominis, obliquus internus abdominis, and transversus abdominis.

    Rectus abdominis
    Obliquus externus abdominis
    Obliquus internus abdominis
    Transversus abdominis
    Other anterior and trunk muscles not considered in this text:
    Intercostals—external and internal—from one rib to another
    Sternocliomastoid
    Scaleni
    Diaphragm

108

FIG. 9-1 • Vertebral column.

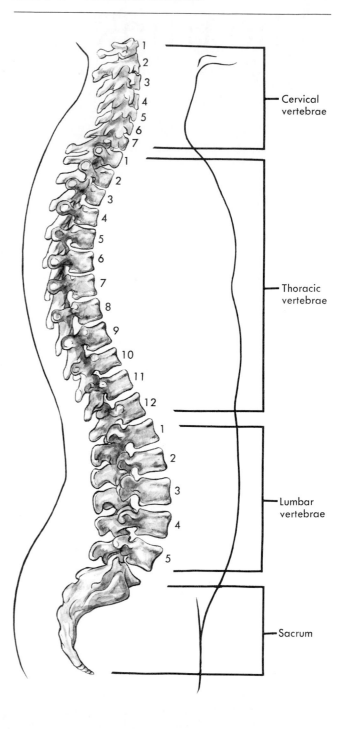

Cervical vertebrae

Thoracic vertebrae

Lumbar vertebrae

Sacrum

FIG. 9-2 • **A,** First cervical vertebra (atlas) viewed from below. **B,**
Third lumbar vertebra viewed from above. **C,** Third lumbar vertebra
viewed from the side.

Modified from Anthony CP and Kolthoff NJ: Textbook of anatomy and physiology, ed. 9, St. Louis, The
CV Mosby Co.

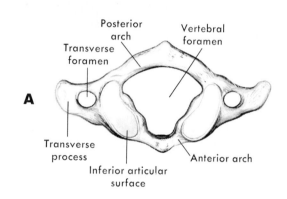

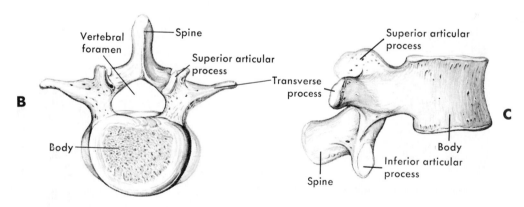

Rectus abdominis muscle FIG. 9-3

Origin

Crest of the pubis.

Insertion

Cartilage of the fifth, sixth, and seventh ribs and the xiphoid process.

Action

Flexion and lateral flexion of the trunk.

Palpation

Anterior-medial surface of the abdomen, between the rib cage and the pubic bone.

Observation and exercise

The rectus abdominis muscle controls the tilt of the pelvis and the consequent curvature of the lower spine. By holding the pelvis up in front, it flattens the lower back. By pulling the pelvis up in front, it makes the erector spinae muscle more effective as an extensor of the spine and also makes the hip flexors (iliopsoas muscle, particularly) more effective in raising the legs.

The controversy as to the best exercises for the abdominal muscles has not been settled. Leg raises, straight-leg sit-ups, bent-knee sit-ups, and isometric contraction are different types of exercises for this region. Bent-knee sit-ups with the arms folded across the chest is considered by many to be best and safest exercise. This exercise largely eliminates the action of the iliopsoas muscle. Twisting to the left and right brings the oblique muscles into more active contraction.

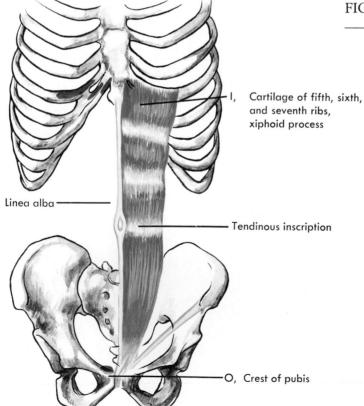

I, Cartilage of fifth, sixth, and seventh ribs, xiphoid process

Linea alba

Tendinous inscription

O, Crest of pubis

FIG. 9-3 • Rectus abdominis muscle.

Obliquus externus abdominis muscle FIG. 9-4

Origin

Borders of the lower eight ribs at the side of the chest dovetailing with the serratus anterior muscle.*

Insertion

Front half of the crest of the ilium, the inguinal ligament, the crest of pubis, and the fascia of the rectus abdominis muscle at the lower front.

---

*Sometimes the origin and insertion are reversed in anatomy books. This is the result of different interpretations given as to which bony structure is the more movable. The insertion is considered the most movable part of a muscle.

Action

Flexes trunk—the right side of the muscle twists to the left, and the left side twists to the right.

Palpation

Lateral side of the abdomen, either left or right.

Observation and exercise

Working on each side of the abdomen, the obliquus externus abdominis muscles aid in twisting the trunk when working independently of each other. Working together, they aid the rectus abdominis muscle in its described action.

The left obliquus externus abdominis muscle comes strongly into contraction during sit-ups when the trunk is twisted to the right, as in touching the left elbow to the right knee. Twisting to the left brings the right obliquus into action.

FIG. 9-4 • Obliquus externus abdominis muscle.

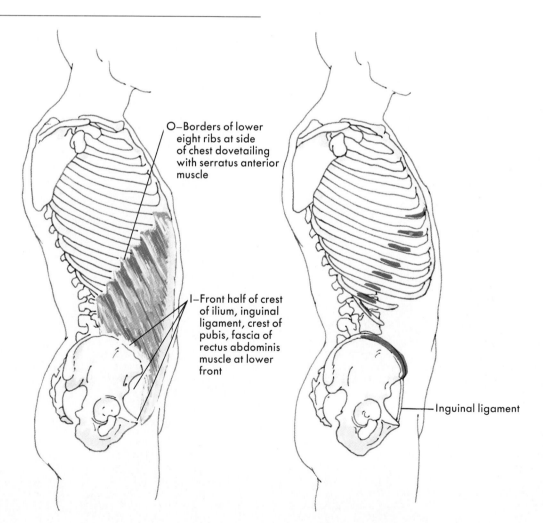

O—Borders of lower eight ribs at side of chest dovetailing with serratus anterior muscle

I—Front half of crest of ilium, inguinal ligament, crest of pubis, fascia of rectus abdominis muscle at lower front

Inguinal ligament

Obliquus internus abdominis muscle FIG. 9-5

Origin

Upper half of the inguinal ligament, anterior two thirds of the crest of the ilium, and the lumbar fascia.

Insertion

Costal cartilages of the eighth, ninth, and tenth ribs and the linea alba.

Action

Flexes trunk—the right side of the muscle twists to the right, and the left side twists to the left.

Palpation

Palpated on the lateral side of the abdomen when the obliquus externus is relaxed.

Observation and exercise

The obliquus internus abdominis muscles run diagonally in the direction opposite to that of the obliquus externus. The left obliquus internus twists to the left, and the right obliquus internus twists to the right.

In touching the left elbow to the right knee in sit-ups, the left obliquus externus and the right obliquus internus abdominis muscles do the twisting at the same time, assisting the rectus abdominis muscle in flexing the trunk to make the completion of the movement possible.

FIG. 9-5 • Obliquus internus abdominis muscle.

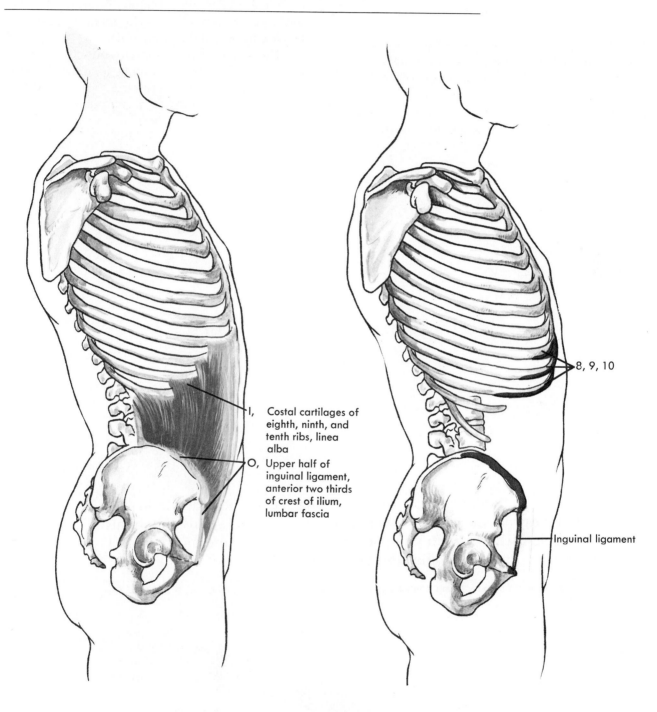

I, Costal cartilages of
eighth, ninth, and
tenth ribs, linea
alba

O, Upper half of
inguinal ligament,
anterior two thirds
of crest of ilium,
lumbar fascia

8, 9, 10

Inguinal ligament

113

Transversus abdominis muscle FIGS. 9-6 and 9-7

Origin

Outer third of the inguinal ligament.
Inner rim of the crest of the ilium.
Inner surface of the cartilage of the lower six ribs.
Lumbar fascia.

Insertion

Crest of the pubis and the iliopectineal line.
Linea alba—joining its fellow from the other side.

Action

Forced expiration by pulling the abdominal wall inward.

Palpation

Cannot be palpated.

Observation and exercise

The transversus abdominis is the chief muscle of forced expiration and is effective, together with the rectus abdominis, obliquus externus abdominis, and obliquus internus abdominis muscles, in helping to hold the abdomen flat.

The transversus abdominis muscle is exercised effectively by attempting to draw the abdominal contents back toward the spine. This may be done isometrically in the supine position or while standing.

FIG. 9-6 • Abdominal wall. Unique arrangement of four abdominal muscles with their fascial attachment in and around rectus abdominis muscle is shown. With no bones for attachments, these muscles can be adequately maintained through exercise.

Modified from Anthony CP and Kolthoff NJ: Textbook of anatomy and physiology, ed. 9, St. Louis, The CV Mosby Co.

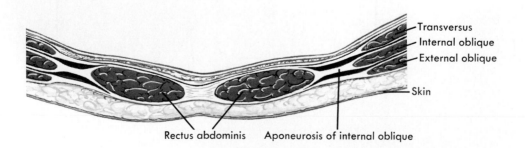

FIG. 9-7 • Transversus abdominis muscle.

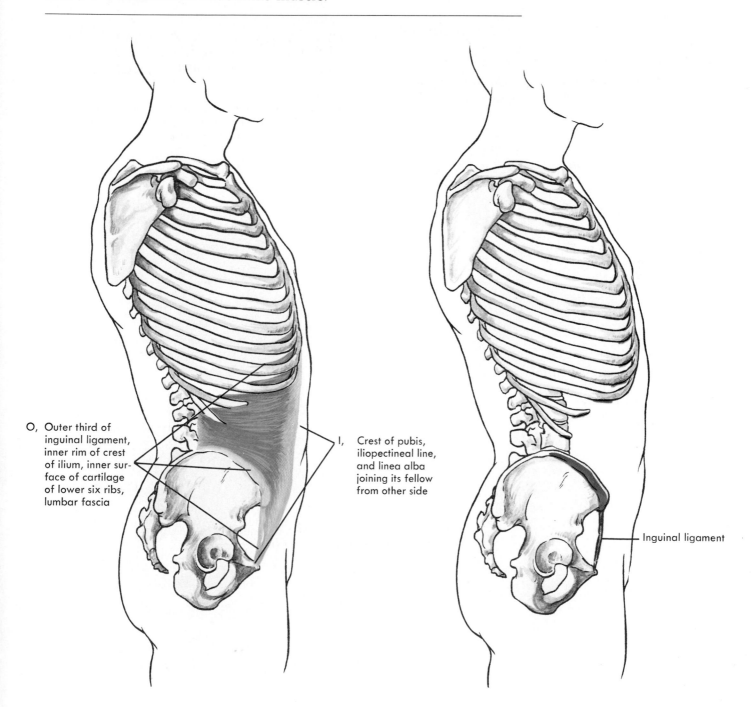

O, Outer third of inguinal ligament, inner rim of crest of ilium, inner surface of cartilage of lower six ribs, lumbar fascia

I, Crest of pubis, iliopectineal line, and linea alba joining its fellow from other side

Inguinal ligament

Quadratus lumborum muscle FIG. 9-8

Origin

Posterior inner lip of the iliac crest and transverse processes of the lower four lumbar vertebrae.

Insertion

Transverse processes of the upper two lumbar vertebrae and lower border of the twelfth rib.

Action

Lateral flexion to the side on which it is located. It stabilizes the pelvis and lumber spine.

Palpation

For all practical purposes, it is impossible to palpate except on an extremely thin individual.

Observation and exercise

The quadratus lumborum is important in lateral trunk flexion.

Trunk twisting and lateral flexion movements are good exercises.

Erector spinae muscle (sacrospinalis)* FIG. 9-9

Origin

Posterior crest of the ilium.

Lower posterior surface of the sacrum.

Inferior borders of the angles of the lower seven ribs.

Spinous processes of all the lumbar and the lower four thoracic vertebrae.

Transverse processes of all the thoracic vertebrae.

---

*This muscle includes the iliocostalis, longissimus dorsi, spinalis dorsi, and divisions of these muscles in the lumbar, thoracic, and cervical sections of the spinal column.

FIG. 9-8 • Quadratus lumborum muscle.

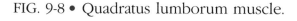

Modified from Anthony CP and Kolthoff NJ: Textbook of anatomy and physiology, ed. 9, St. Louis, The CV Mosby Co.

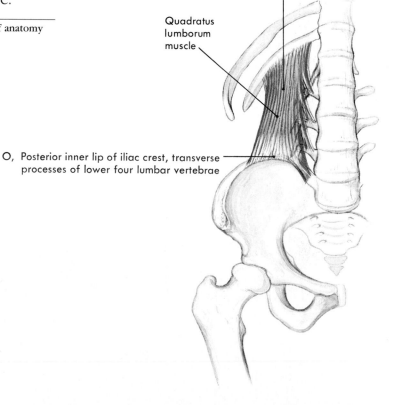

I, Transverse processes of upper two lumbar vertebrae and lower border of twelfth rib

Quadratus lumborum muscle

O, Posterior inner lip of iliac crest, transverse processes of lower four lumbar vertebrae

Insertion

Angles of the ribs.
Transverse process of all the vertebrae.
Base of the skull toward the mastoid process.

Action

Extension of the spine and inclination of the head backward. Lateral flexion with abdominals to the side of its location.

Palpation

Lower lumbar region on either side of the spine.

Observation and exercise

The erector spinae muscle functions best when the pelvis is held up in front, thus pulling it down slightly in back. This lowers the origin of the erector spinae and makes it more effective in keeping the spine straight. As the spine is held straight, the ribs are raised, thus fixing the chest high and consequently making the abdominal muscles more effective in holding the pelvis up in front and flattening the abdominal wall.

An exercise known as "dead lift," employing a barbell, localizes the action in the erector spinae. In this exercise the subject bends over, keeping the arms and legs straight, picks up the barbell, and returns to a standing position. Voluntary static contraction of the erector spinae in the standing position would provide a mild exercise and improve body posture.

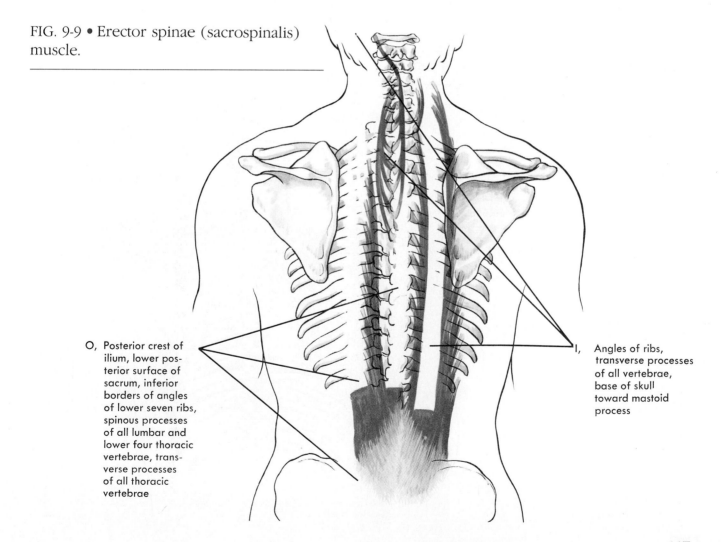

FIG. 9-9 • Erector spinae (sacrospinalis) muscle.

O, Posterior crest of ilium, lower posterior surface of sacrum, inferior borders of angles of lower seven ribs, spinous processes of all lumbar and lower four thoracic vertebrae, transverse processes of all thoracic vertebrae

I, Angles of ribs, transverse processes of all vertebrae, base of skull toward mastoid process

Splenius muscles (cervicis, capitis) FIG. 9-10

Origin

Lower half of the ligamentum nuchae and spinous processes of the seventh cervical and the upper five thoracic vertebrae.

Insertion

Transverse processes of the upper four cervical vertebrae and base of the skull toward the mastoid process.

Action

Extension of the head and neck—pulling on one side bends the head sidward and backward and tends to twist right on the right side and left on the left side.

Palpation

Cannot be palpated.

Observation and exercise

Bridging would bring the splenius muscle strongly into play, together with the erector spinae and the upper trapezius muscles. Tone in the splenius muscle tends to hold the head and neck in proper posture position.

FIG. 9-10 • Splenius muscles (cervicis, capitis).

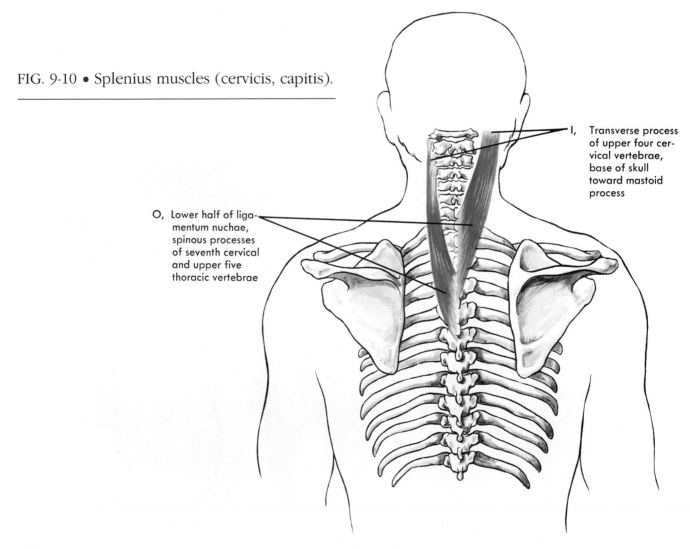

I, Transverse process of upper four cervical vertebrae, base of skull toward mastoid process

O, Lower half of ligamentum nuchae, spinous processes of seventh cervical and upper five thoracic vertebrae

Exercise

Bridging, as just mentioned, is a good exercise. If bridging is too difficult, one should just attempt to bridge by taking as much of the body weight as possible on the back of the head and the soles of the feet while lying on the back with the knees flexed. A more moderate exercise for the splenius muscle is to lace the fingers behind the head and statically contract the posterior head and neck muscles: deltoideus, teres major, triceps, erector spinal, trapezius, and others.

Muscle identification

In Fig. 9-11, identify muscles of the trunk, shoulder girdle, and shoulder joint: deltoideus, teres major, triceps, erector spinae, trapezius, and others.

Laboratory and review exercises

As an aid to student learning and for assignments; in-class, out-of-class or for teacher testing tear-out sheet worksheets are found at the end of the text (pages 177-178).

Anterior skeletal worksheet (no. 1)

Draw and label the following muscles on the skeletal chart
a. Rectus abdominus
b. Oblique externus abdominis
c. Oblique internus abdominis

Posterior skeletal worksheet (no. 2)

Draw and label the following muscles on the skeletal chart
a. Erector spinae
b. Quadrus lumborum
c. Splenius—cervicis and capitis

FIG. 9-11 • Muscles of trunk, shoulder joint, and shoulder girdle.

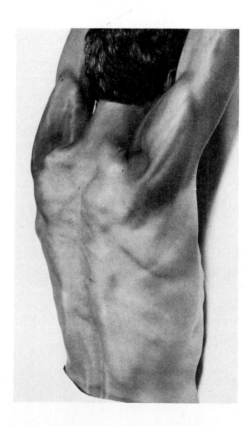

Additional laboratory and review exercises

1. Locate the following parts of the trunk on a human skeleton and human subject.
   a. Cervical vertebra
   b. Thoracic vertebra
   c. Lumbar vertebra
   d. Spinous process
   e. Transverse process
   f. Sacrum
   e. Manubrium
   g. Xiphoid process
   h. Sternum
   i. Rib cage (various ribs)

2. How and where do you palpate the following muscles on a human subject?
   a. Rectus abdominis
   b. Obliquus externus abdominis
   c. Erector spinae
   d. Quadratus lumborum
3. Contrast bent-knee sit-ups with straight-leg sit-ups.
4. Which exercise is better for the development of the abdominal muscles—leg-lifts or sit-ups? Defend your answer.
5. Why is good abdominal muscular development so important? Why is this area so frequently neglected?
6. Why are weak abdominal muscles frequently blamed for lower back pains?
7. Prepare an oral or written report on abdominal or back injuries found in the literature.
8. Fill in the movements and muscle actions of the trunk on the chart below. List the muscles primarily responsible for each movement.

Muscle analysis chart • Trunk

Trunk	
Flexion	Extension
Lateral flexion right	Rotation right
Lateral flexion left	Rotation left

References

Day AL: Observation on the treatment of lumbar disc disease in college football players, American Journal of Sports Medicine, 15:7275, January-February 1987.

Holden DL and Jackson DW: Stress fractures of ribs in female rowers, American Journal of Sports Medicine, 13:277, July-August 1987.

Martens MA et al: Adductor tendonitus and muscular abdominis tendopathy, American Journal of Sports Medicine, 15:353, July-August 1987.

Marymont JV: Exercise-related stress reaction of the sacroilian joint, an unusual cause of low back pain in athletes, American Journal of Sports Medicine, 14:320, July-August 1986.

Muscular analysis of selected exercises and activities

10

Student objectives

• To understand the overload principle and how to apply it to strengthening major muscle groups.

• To know and understand the different types of muscle contractions.

• To learn to analyze an exercise for major joint movements.

• To know and understand the most important major muscles responsible for joint actions.

• To learn to analyze and prescribe exercises to strengthen all major muscle groups.

Chapter 5 presented an introduction to the analysis of exercise and activities. That chapter included only the analysis of the muscles previously studied in the shoulder region. Since that chapter, all the other joints and big muscle groups of the human body have been considered. The exercises and activities found in this chapter consider muscles in other parts of the body, as well as further analysis of shoulder area muscles.

Strength and endurance of the muscles of the lower extremity, trunk, and abdominal sections are also very important in skillful physical performance and body maintenance.

Concentric and eccentric contraction are basic in this section of the body too. Concentric contraction is a shortening contraction of the muscles, whereas eccentric contraction is a condition in which the muscle returns to its original length. Contraction against gravity is quite evident in the lower extremities too.

The quadriceps muscle group contracts eccentrically when the body is being lowered in a weight-bearing movement through leg action. Knee joint flexion in weight-bearing movements involves quadriceps eccentric contraction and prevents too rapid a downward movement. One can easily demonstrate this fact by palpating this muscle group when moving from a standing position to a half squat. Almost as much work is done in this type of contraction as in concentric contraction.

In recent years more and more muscle educators on all levels have been emphasizing the development of local muscle groups through weight-training and circuit-training activities. Athletes and nonathletes, both boys and girls, need to have overall muscular development. Sport participation will not ensure sufficient development of local muscle groups. Also, more and more emphasis has been placed on mechanical kinesiology in physical education and athletic skill teaching. This is desirable and can help bring about more skillful performance, but one must remember that mechanical principles will be of little or no value to performers without adequate strength and endurance of their muscular system, which is developed through planned exercises and activities.

In the physical revolution of recent years, a much greater emphasis has been placed on exercises and activities that improve the physical fitness, strength, and endurance of participants. This chapter will continue the practice of analyzing the muscles through simple exercises that began in Chapter 5. When these techniques are mastered, the individual is ready to analyze and prescribe exercises and activities for muscular strength and endurance needed in sport activities and for healthful living.

Overload principle

A basic physiological principle of exercise is the overload principle. It states that a muscle or muscle group increases in strength in direct proportion to the overload placed on it. To improve the strength and functioning of major muscles, muscle educators need to apply this principle to every large muscle group in the body, progressively, at all age levels, and year after year. Increasing the speed of doing the exercise, the number of repetitions, the weight, and more bouts of isometric contractions are all ways to apply this principle. Many coaches are having their athletes perform various weight-training activities (overload principle) during season to improve the strength of muscle groups.

Muscular development

For years it was thought that a person developed adequate muscular strength through participation in sport activities. Now the philosophy is that one develops muscular strength to be able to adequately participate in sport activities.

Adequate muscular strength of the entire body from head to toe should be developed. Individuals responsible for this development need to prescribe exercises that will meet this objective.

In schools, this development should start at an early age and continue throughout the school years. Fitness tests have found that there is need for considerable improvement in this area. The chin-up (pull-up) test had to be modified as more than 50% of children could not do one chin. Sit-up, standing broad jump, mile run, and other tests all indicated fitness deficiencies in the children of United States. Adequate muscular strength and endurance are important in the adult years. Many back pains and other physical ailments could be avoided.

The exercises in this chapter will help individuals learn how to analyze and prescribe exercises for overall muscular development for young and old.

Sit-up
Description

The subject lies on the back, fingers interlaced behind the neck, with the legs straight and the feet about hip-width apart. He curls up to a sitting position, twists the trunk to the left, touches the right elbow to the left knee, and then returns to the starting position.

Analysis

This exercise is divided into four movements for analysis: (1) curling movement to sitting-up position, (2) twisting movement to left, (3) return movement to sitting-up position, and (4) return movement to starting position.

Curling movement to sitting-up position
  Trunk
    Flexion
      Rectus abdominis
      Iliopsoas
      Obliquus externus abdominis
      Obliquus internus abdominis
Twisting movement to left
  Trunk
    Left lateral rotation and flexion
      Left rectus abdominis
      Right obliquus externus abdominis
      Left obliquus internus abdominis
      Left erector spinae
  Right shoulder joint
    Adduction and flexion
      Pectoralis major
      Anterior deltoideus
      Latissimus dorsi
      Teres major
  Left shoulder joint
    Abduction and extension
      Latissimus dorsi
      Teres major
      Posterior deltoideus
      Pectoralis major
  Right shoulder girdle
    Abduction and lateral tilt
      Trapezius
      Serratus anterior
      Pectoralis minor
  Left shoulder girdle
    Abduction and reduction of lateral tilt
      Rhomboideus major
      Rhomboideus minor
      Trapezius (lower)
Return movement to sitting-up position
  Trunk
    Right lateral rotation and flexion
      Right rectus abdominis
      Left obliquus externus abdominis
      Right obliquus internus abdominis
      Right erector spinae
  Right shoulder joint
    Abduction and extension
      Latissimus dorsi
      Teres major
      Posterior deltoideus
      Pectoralis major

Left shoulder joint
  Adduction and flexion
    Pectoralis major
    Anterior deltoideus
    Latissimus dorsi
    Teres major
Right shoulder girdle
  Adduction and reduction of lateral tilt
    Rhomboideus major
    Rhomboideus minor
    Trapezius (lower)
Left shoulder girdle
  Adduction and depression
    Trapezius
    Serratus anterior
    Pectoralis minor
Return movement to starting position
  Trunk
    Extension—trunk flexors (eccentric contraction)
      Rectus abdominis
      Obliquus externus abdominis
      Obliquus internus abdominals
      Iliopsoas

Sit-up—bent knee
Description

The subject lies on the back, fingers interlocked behind the neck, with legs flexed at the knee and feet approximately 1 foot apart. NOTE: The slight movement of the arms and shoulder area in this exercise will be ignored in this analysis.

Analysis

This exercise is divided into two movements for analysis: (1) curling movement to sitting-up position, and (2) return movement to starting position.
Curling movement to sitting-up position
  Trunk
    Flexion—rectus abdominis
      Obliquus externus abdominis
      Obliquus internus abdominis
      Iliopsoas
Return movement to starting position
  Trunk
    Extension—trunk flexors (eccentric contraction)
      Rectus abdominis
      Obliquus externus abdominis
      Obliquus internus abdominis
      Iliopsoas

Prone arch

Description

The subject lies in a prone position, face down, with the hands tucked under the thighs. The head, shoulders, and legs are raised from the floor. The legs are kept straight. Then the subject returns to the starting position.

Analysis

This exercise is divided into two movements for analysis: (1) movement to raise head, trunk, and legs, and (2) return movement to starting position.

Movement to raise head, trunk, and legs
- **Trunk and head**
  - Extension
    - Erector spinae
    - Splenius
    - Quadratus lumborum
- **Hip**
  - Extension
    - Gluteus maximus
    - Hamstrings

Return movement to starting position
- **Trunk and head**
  - Flexion
    - Trunk and head extensors (eccentric contraction)
- **Hip**
  - Flexion
    - Hip extensors (eccentric contraction)

BARBELL WEIGHT-TRAINING EXERCISES*

Exercise through the use of weights has become increasingly important as a means of developing and maintaining muscular strength in young people and adults. When this type of exercise is undertaken, a thorough knowledge of the muscles being used is essential so that one group of muscles will not be overdeveloped and another underdeveloped.

Most schools have barbells available for use by students. Some physical education teachers and coaches recommend that junior and senior high school students have their own barbell set for use at home.

An analysis of several selected weight-training exercises will introduce the muscular analysis of these activities. In these exercises the only equipment needed is a barbell with weights.

---

*These are only sample weight-training exercises. Students are encouraged to continue the study of muscular analysis of the many other weight-training exercises and activities.

Arm curl

Description

With the subject in a standing position, the barbell is held in the hands with the palms to the front. The barbell is curled upward and forward until the forearms are completely flexed. Then it is returned to the starting position.

Analysis

This exercise is divided into two movements for analysis: (1) upward curl movement, and (2) return movement to starting position. NOTE: An assumption is made that no movement occurs in the shoulder joint and shoulder girdle.

Upward curl movement
  Wrist and hand
    Flexion
      Wrist and hand flexors
  Elbow joint
    Flexion
      Biceps brachii
      Brachialis
      Brachioradialis
      Pronator teres
Return movement to starting position
  Wrist and hand
    Extension
      Wrist and hand flexors (eccentric contraction)
  Elbow joint
    Extension
      Elbow joint flexors (eccentric contraction)

FIG. 10-1 • Barbell press.

Press   FIG. 10-1

Description

The barbell is held in a position high in front of the chest with palms facing forward, feet comfortably spread, and back and legs straight. From this position it is pushed upward until the arms are fully extended overhead, and then it is returned to the starting position.

Analysis

This exercise is divided into two movements for analysis: (1) upward movement and (2) return movement to starting position.
Upward movement
  Wrist and hand
    No movement
      Wrist and hand flexors (continued contraction)
  Elbow joint
    Extension
      Triceps brachii
      Anconeus
  Shoulder joint
    Flexion
      Pectoralis major
      Anterior deltoideus
      Biceps brachii
  Shoulder girdle
    Elevation
      Trapezius
      Rhomboideus major
      Rhomboideus minor
      Levator scapulae
Return movement to starting position
  Wrist and hand
    No movement
  Elbow joint
    Flexion
      Elbow joint extensors (eccentric contraction)
  Shoulder joint
    Extension
      Shoulder joint flexors (eccentric contraction)
  Shoulder girdle
    Adduction and depression
      Shoulder girdle elevators (eccentric contraction)

Squat

Description

The subject places a barbell on the shoulders behind the neck and grasps it with the palms-forward position of the hands. He squats down until the thighs are parallel to the floor, keeping the back straight, and then returns to the starting position.

Analysis

This exercise is divided into two movements for analysis: (1) movement to knee-bend position, and (2) return movement to starting position. NOTE: It is assumed that no movement will take place in the shoulder joint, shoulder girdle, wrists, hands, and back.

Movement to knee-bend position
> **Hip**
>> Flexion
>>> Hip extensors (eccentric contraction)
>>> Gluteus maximus
>>> Hamstrings
>
> **Knee**
>> Flexion
>>> Knee extensors (eccentric contraction)
>>> Quadriceps
>
> **Foot and ankle**
>> Plantar flexion
>>> Gastrocnemius
>>> Peroneus longus
>>> Soleus

Return movement to starting position
> **Hip**
>> Extension
>>> Gluteus maximus
>>> Hamstrings
>
> **Knee**
>> Extension
>>> Quadriceps
>
> **Foot and ankle**
>> Dorsal flexion
>>> Plantar flexors (eccentric contraction)

Dead lift

Description

The subject is in a standing position with the barbell held in the hands. He bends over, keeping the arms and legs straight, and touches the floor with the barbell. Then a movement to the standing position is made.

Analysis

This exercise is divided into two movements for analysis: (1) movement to bend over and to touch the barbell to the floor, and (2) return movement to standing position.

Movement to bend over and to touch barbell to floor
> **Wrist and hand**
>> Flexion
>>> Wrist and hand flexors
>
> **Trunk**
>> Flexion
>>> Trunk extensors (eccentric contraction)
>>> Erector spinae (sacrospinalis)
>>> Quadratus lumborum
>>> Splenius

NOTE: Slight movement (if any) of the shoulder joint and girdle is not being analyzed.

Return movement to standing position
> **Wrist and hand**
>> Flexion
>>> Wrist and hand flexors
>
> **Trunk**
>> Extension
>>> Erector spinae (sacrospinalis)
>>> Quadratus lumborum
>>> Splenius

ISOMETRIC EXERCISES

An exercise technique called "isometrics" is a type of muscular activity in which there is contraction of muscle groups with little or no muscle shortening. Many magazine articles and books have been written about isometric exercises and their values. They are, without doublt, an effective way to build and maintain muscular strength.

A few selected isometric exercises will be analyzed muscularly to show how they are designed to develop specific muscle groups.

Abdominal contraction

Description

The subject contracts the muscles in the anterior abdominal region as strongly as possible with no movement of the trunk or hips. This exercise can be performed in sitting, standing, or supine positions. The longer the contraction in seconds, the more valuable the exercise will be, to a degree.

Analysis

Abdomen
    Contraction
        Rectus abdominis
        Obliquus externus abdominis
        Obliquus internus abdominis
        Transversus abdominis

Shoulder pull

Description

In a standing or sitting position, the subject clasps the hands together in front of the chest and then attempts to pull them apart. This contraction is continued from 5 to 20 seconds.

Analysis

In this type of exercise there is little or no movement of the contracting muscles. In certain isometric exercises, contraction of the antagonistic muscles is as strong as the muscles attempting to produce the force for movement. The muscle groups contracting to produce a movement are designated the *agonists*. In the exercise just described, there are contractions of the antagonistic muscles of the wrist and hand, elbow, shoulder joint, and shoulder girdle. The strength of the contraction depends on the angle of pull and the leverage of the joint involved. Thus it is not the same at each point.

Attempted movements
    Extension of wrist and hand—resisted by flexors of wrist and hand
        Agonists—wrist and hand extensors
        Antagonists—wrist and hand flexors
    Extension of elbow joint—resisted by flexors of wrist, elbow, and hand
        Agonists—triceps brachi and anconeus
        Antagonists—biceps brachii, brachialis, brachioradialis, pronator teres
    Abduction of shoulder joint—resisted by adductors of shoulder joint
        Agonists—teres major, latissimus dorsi, posterior deltoideus
        Antagonists—pectoralis major and anterior deltoideus
    Adduction and depression of shoulder girdle—resisted by abductors
        Agonists—rhomboideus major, rhomboideus minor, trapezius
        Antagonists—serratus anterior, pectoralis minor, trapezius (upper)

Isometric exercises vary in the number of muscles contracting, depending on the type of exercise and the joints at which there is attempted movement. The shoulder-pull exercise produces some contraction of antagonistic muscles at four joints.

Leg lifter*

Description

The subject sits on a bench or chair with the knees slightly bent and with one leg over the other. He attempts to raise the left leg while resisting it with the right leg.

Analysis

Left leg—attempted upward movement
Foot and ankle
Plantar flexion
Gastrocnemius
Peroneus longus
Soleus
Knee
Extension
Quadriceps
Rectus femoris
Vastus medialis
Vastus lateralis
Vastus intermedius
Hips
Flexion
Iliopsoas
Sartorius
Tensor fasciae latae
Right leg—resisting upward movement
Foot and ankle
Plantar flexion
Gastrocnemius
Peroneus longus
Soleus
Knee
Flexion
Hamstrings
Biceps femoris
Semitendinosus
Semimembranosus
Hip
Extension
Gluteus maximus
Hamstrings

---

*When the legs are alternated, the muscles used will be the same muscles but in the other leg.

UNIVERSAL CONDITIONING MACHINE

The Universal conditioning machine* (Fig. 10-2) is used by professional, college, and many high school athletes. Health clubs, YMCAs, YWCAs, and "body shops" have these machines for use by their members. Many similar types of machines are available; these include Cybex, Nautilus, Olympus, and others.

All exercise machines come with a list of recommended exercises that can be done by the user. A few of the exercises for the Universal conditioning machine are analyzed in the following section. Figure 10-3 is a daily record sheet that can be kept by the participant.

---

*Universal Athletics Sales Co., Inc., Fresno, Calif.

FIG. 10-2 • Universal conditioning machine
with 16 separate stations.

Courtesy Universal Athletic Sales Co., Inc., Fresno, Calif.

Features of the Universal Gym Machine are protected by one or more U.S. patents
2,932,509 3,116,062; other patents allowed and other patents pending.

1. Leg press

2. Chest press

3. Shoulder press

4. High lateral pull

5. Quad and dead lift
   station

6. Chinning station

7. Dipping station

8. Hip flexor

9. Abdominal conditioner

10. Thigh and knee machine

11. Back hyperextension
    and swimmers' kick station

12. Wrist conditioner

13. Hand gripper station

14. Neck conditioner

15. Hand gripper station

16. Real-runner

FIG. 10-3 • Universal Spartacus daily record sheet.

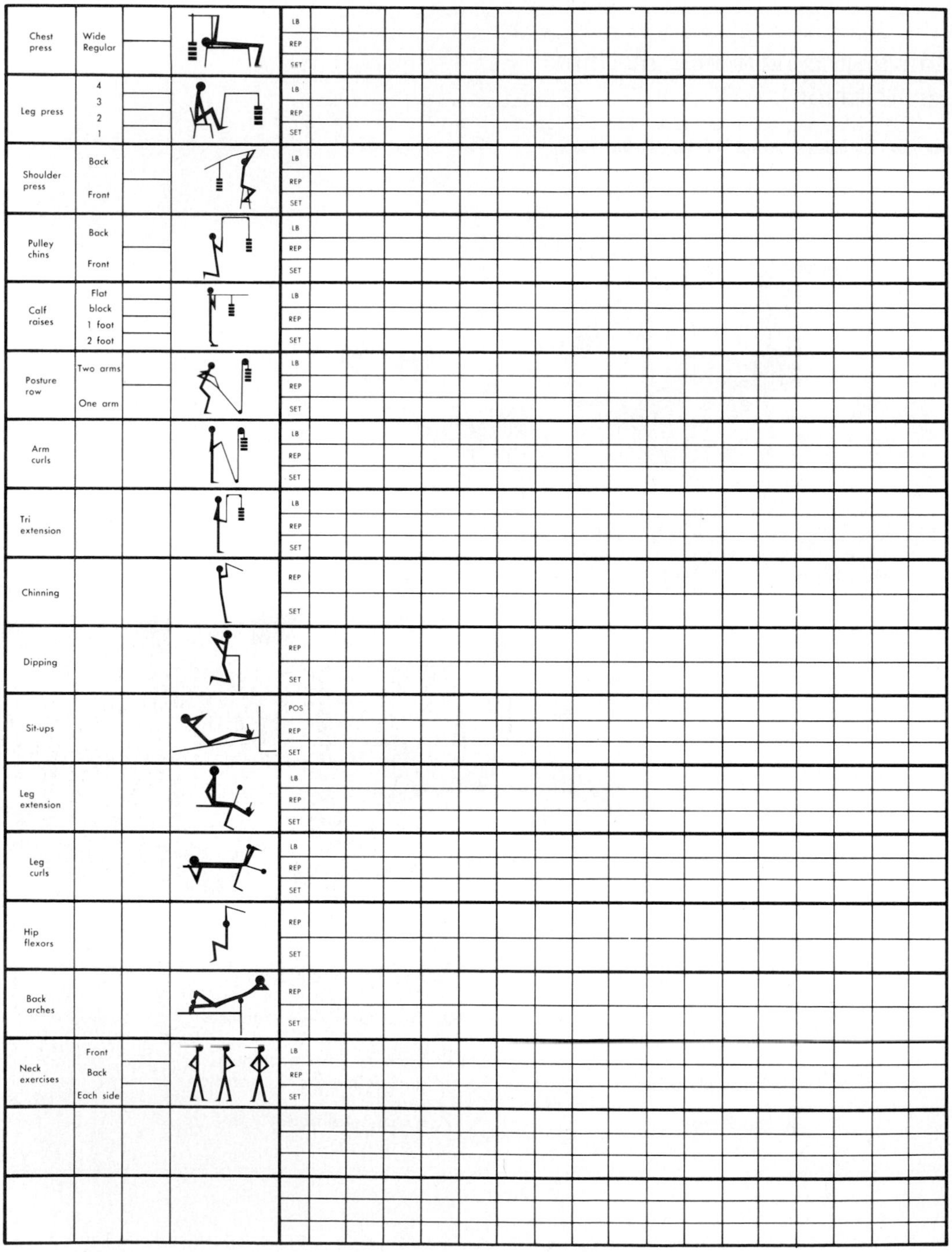

Chest press	Wide Regular			LB																		
				REP																		
				SET																		
Leg press	4 3 2 1			LB																		
				REP																		
				SET																		
Shoulder press	Back Front			LB																		
				REP																		
				SET																		
Pulley chins	Back Front			LB																		
				REP																		
				SET																		
Calf raises	Flat block 1 foot 2 foot			LB																		
				REP																		
				SET																		
Posture row	Two arms One arm			LB																		
				REP																		
				SET																		
Arm curls				LB																		
				REP																		
				SET																		
Tri extension				LB																		
				REP																		
				SET																		
Chinning				REP																		
				SET																		
Dipping				REP																		
				SET																		
Sit-ups				POS																		
				REP																		
				SET																		
Leg extension				LB																		
				REP																		
				SET																		
Leg curls				LB																		
				REP																		
				SET																		
Hip flexors				REP																		
				SET																		
Back arches				REP																		
				SET																		
Neck exercises	Front Back Each side			LB																		
				REP																		
				SET																		

Leg press

Description

The subject sits and presses until the knees are straight. Then he returns to the starting position.

Analysis

Leg press can be divided into two movements for analysis: (1) movement to straight-leg position, and (2) return to starting position (Fig. 10-4).

Movement to straight-leg position

  Foot and ankle
    No movement
  Knee
    Extension
      Quadriceps
  Hip
    Extension
      Hamstrings
      Gluteus maximus
      Adductor magnus

Return to starting position

  Foot and ankle
    No movement
  Knee
    Flexion
      Knee extensors (eccentric contraction)
  Hip
    Flexion
      Hip extensors (eccentric contraction)

FIG. 10-4 • Leg press.

Triceps extension

Description

The subject stands in front of the machine with the arms flexed at the elbow, grasps the bar, and presses down until the arms are straight.

Analysis

This exercise can be divided into two movements for analysis: (1) movement to pressing arms down to straight-arm position and (2) return movement to starting position.

Movement to straight-arm position
Wrist and hand
Flexion
Wrist and hand flexors
Elbow joint
Extension
Triceps brachii
Anconeus
Shoulder joint
Extension
Latissimus dorsi
Teres major
Posterior deltoideus
Pectoralis major
Triceps brachii (long head)

Shoulder girdle
Adduction and depression
Lower trapezius
Pectoralis minor
Return movement to starting position
Wrist and hand
Flexion
Wrist and hand flexors
Elbow joint
Flexion
Elbow joint extensors
(eccentric contraction)
Shoulder joint
Flexion
Shoulder joint extensors
(eccentric contraction)
Shoulder girdle abductors
Abduction and tilting
Shoulder girdle abductors
(eccentric contraction)

Chest press

Description

The subject lies on the exercise bench in the supine position, grasps the apparatus hand holds, and presses the weight upward through the full range of arm and shoulder movement. Then the weight is lowered to the starting position (Fig. 10-2).

Analysis

The chest press can be divided into two movements for analysis: (1) upward movement to length of arms, and (2) return movement to the starting position.

Movement to upward position
   Wrist and hand
      Flexion
         Wrist and hand flexors
   Elbow joint
      Extension
         Triceps
         Anconeus
   Shoulder joint
      Flexion and horizontal flexion
         Pectoralis major
         Anterior deltoideus
         Biceps brachii

Shoulder girdle
   Abduction and lateral tilting
      Serratus anterior
      Pectoralis minor
Return movement to starting position
   Wrist and hands
      Flexion
         Wrist and hand flexors
   Elbow joint
      Flexion
         Elbow joint extensors (eccentric contraction)
   Shoulder joint
      Extension and horizontal extension
         Shoulder joint flexors (eccentric contraction)
   Shoulder girdle
      Adduction and depression
         Shoulder girdle abductors (eccentric contraction)

Modern exercise machines

With the physical revolution of the past several decades has come the development of many new exercise machines. Some machines are engineered to have a constant resistance throughout the range of movement. A number of companies have developed individual machines for exercising many of the big muscle groups of the human body: quadriceps, hamstrings, abdominals, neck, pectoral, and other muscle groups.

Hip sled (leg and hip press) (Fig. 10-5)

Description

The subject lies in a supine position on the floor with the knees and hips flexed in a position close to the chest. The feet are placed on the apparatus plate. The plate is moved upward until the knees and hips are completely extended. Then the subject returns to the starting position.

Analysis

This exercise is divided into two movements for analysis: (1) movement upward to high position, and (2) return movement to the starting position.

Movement upward to high position

Foot and ankle

Plantar flexion (slight)

Gastrocnemius, soleus, tibialis posterior, peroneus longus

Knee

Extension

Quadriceps (rectus femoris, vastus medialis, vastus intermedius, vastus lateralis)

Hip

Extension

Hamstrings (biceps femoris, semimembranosus, semitendinosus) gluteus maximus

Return movement to the starting position

Foot and ankle

Dorsal flexion (eccentric plantar flexors)

Knee

Flexion

Knee extendors (eccentric contraction)

Hip

Flexion

Hip extendors (eccentric contraction)

A

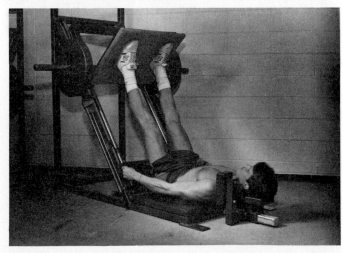

B

FIG. 10-5 • Hip sled (hip and leg press.) **A,** Starting position. **B,** High position.

Rowing exercise

Description

The subject sits on a movable seat with the knees and hips flexed close to the chest. The arms are reaching forward (Fig. 10-5) to grasp a horizontal bar. The legs are extended forcibly as the arms are pulled toward the chest. Then the legs and arms are returned to the starting position. The machine is engineered to provide variable resistance to the movements of the upper and lower extremities.

Analysis

The exercise is divided into two movements for analysis: (1) movement to extend the legs forward and arms pulled toward the chest, and (2) return to the starting position.

Movement to extend the legs forward and arms pulled toward the chest.

Foot and ankle
  No movement

Knee
  Extension
    Quadriceps (rectus femoris, vastus medialis, vastus intermedius, vastus lateralis)

Hip
  Extension
    Hamstrings (biceps femoris, semimembranosus, semitendinosus), gluteus maximus

Trunk
  Extension
    Erector spinae

Shoulder girdle
  Adduction and depression
    Trapezius (lower)
    Rhomboideus

Shoulder joint
  Extension
    Latissimus dorsi, teres major, posterior deltoid, teres minor, infraspinatus

Elbow joint
  Flexion
    Biceps brachii, brachialis, brachioradiatis, pronator teres

Wrist and hand
  Flexion
    Wrist and hand flexors

Return to the starting position

Foot and ankle
  No movement

Knee
  Flexion
    Eccentric contraction (knee joint extendors)

Hip
  Flexion
    Hip extensors (eccentric contraction)

Trunk
  Flexion
    Trunk extensors (eccentric contraction)

Shoulder girdle
  Abduction and elevation
    Shoulder girdle extensors (eccentric contraction)

Shoulder joint
  Flexion
    Shoulder joint extensors (eccentric contraction)

Elbow joint
  Extension
    Shoulder joint flexors (eccentric contraction)

Wrist and hands
  Flexion
    Wrist and hand flexors

FIG. 10-6 • Rowing exercise machine. **A,**
Starting position. **B,** Movement.

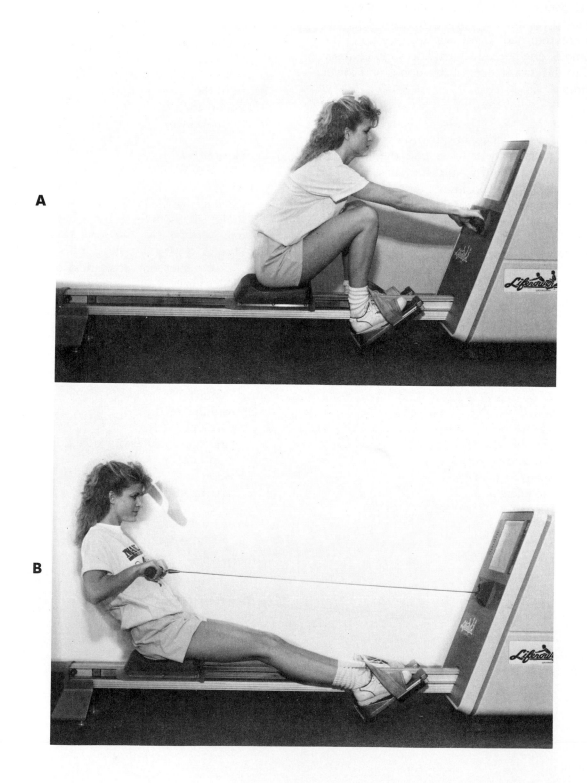

Laboratory and review exercises

As an aid to student learning and for assignments, in-class, out-of-class, or for teacher testing, take any exercise from the Universal Spartacus daily record sheet.

1. Using the techniques taught in this chapter and Chapter 5, analyze the joint movements and muscles used in the exercise.

Additional laboratory and review exercises

1. Obtain, describe, and completely analyze five conditioning exercises.
2. Collect, analyze, and evaluate exercises that are found in newspapers and magazines or are observed on television.
3. Prepare a set of exercises that will ensure development of all big muscle groups in the body.
4. Select exercises from exercise books for analysis.
5. Bring to class other typical exercises for members to analyze.
6. Analyze the conditioning exercises given by your physical education teachers or varsity coaches.
7. Observe children using playground equipment. Analyze muscularly the activities they are performing.
8. Visit the room on your campus where the heavy apparatus (Universal or similar machine) is located. Analyze exercises that can be done with the machine.
9. Consider a sport (basketball or any other sport) and develop exercises applying the overload principle that would develop all the big muscle groups used in the sport.

NOTE: Manufacturers of all types of exercise apparatus have a complete list of exercises that can be performed with their machines. Secure a copy of recommended exercises and muscularly analyze each exercise.

References

Baitch SP: Aerobic dance injuries, a biomechanical approach, Journal of Physical Education, Recreation and Dance 58:57, May-June 1987.

Bouche J: Three essential lifts for high school players, Scholastic Coach, 56:42, April 1987.

Brzycki C: R$_x$ for a safe productive strength program, Scholastic Coach, September 1987.

Epley B: Getting elementary muscles, Coach and Athlete, November-December 1981.

Matheson O, et al: Stress fractures in athletes, American Journal of Sports Medicine 15:46, January-February 1987.

Minton S: Dance dynamics—avoiding dance injuries (symposium), Journal of Physical Education, Recreation and Dance 58:29, May-June 1987.

Schlitz J: The athlete's daily dozen stretches, Athletic Journal 66:20, November 1985.

Todd J: Strength training for female athletes, Journal of Physical Education, Recreation and Dance, 56:38, August 1985.

Some factors affecting motion and movement

11

Student objectives

- To know and understand how knowledge of the laws of levers can help improve physical performance.

- To know and understand how knowledge of Newton's laws of motion can help improve physical performance.

- To know and understand how knowledge of balance and force can help improve physical performance.

Many students in kinesiology classes have some knowledge, from a college or high school physics or physical science course, of the physical laws that affect motion. However, they need to review these facts and principles in light of applying them to motion in the human body. A brief discussion of some of these principles follows.

FIG. 11-1 • First-class lever.

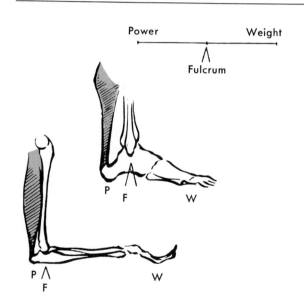

Levers

It is difficult for a person to visualize his body as a system of levers. The topic may seem academic to some, but this is far from true. A person moves through the use of his system of levers. The anatomical levers of the body cannot be changed, but a more efficient use of the system can be made when it is understood.

A lever is defined as a rigid bar that turns about an axis. In the body, the bones represent the bars and the joints are the axes. Contractions of muscles provide the force to move the levers. A lever has three points that determine which type of lever it is and for which kind of motion it is best suited. These points are the axis, or fulcrum (the point of rotation), the point of force application (usually the muscle insertion), and the point of resistance application (sometimes the center of gravity of the lever and sometimes the location of an external resistance). The three possible position combinations (Figs. 11-1 to 11-3) of these three points on a lever produce a first-class lever with the axis between the force *(F)* and the resistance *(R)*, a second-class lever with the resistance between the axis and the force, and a third-class lever with the force between the axis and the resistance.

First-class levers

A first-class lever (Fig. 11-1) is designed basically to produce balanced movements when the axis is midway between the force and the resistance. When the axis is close to the force, the lever produces speed and range of motion. When the axis is close to the resistance, the lever produces force motion. Typical examples of a first-class lever are the crowbar, seesaw, and elbow extension.

The important thing to remember in applying the principle of levers to the body is that the power is applied where the muscle inserts in the bone and not in the belly of the muscle. For example, in the triceps of the elbow action, power is applied on the olecranon of the ulna behind the elbow joint, the axis with the weight of the forearm being moved by the principle of this lever.

As power in excess of resistance is applied at point *P* (Fig. 11-1) from above, the olecranon is pulled up and the arm descends. This is called "extension."

The same principle applies to the ankle in extension of the unsupported foot by the gastrocnemius and soleus muscles. When the gastrocnemius and soleus pull on the heel, or calcaneus, from above, the foot goes down with the ankle as an axis.

Second-class levers

A second-class lever (Fig. 11-2) is designed to produce force movements, since a large resistance can be moved by a relatively small force. An example of a second-class lever is a wheelbarrow. A rare example of a second-class lever in the body is plantar flexion of the supported foot. The ball of the foot is the axis, the articulation of the tibia with the foot is the resistance, and the pull of the plantar flexors on the calcaneus is the force.

FIG. 11-2 • Second-class lever.

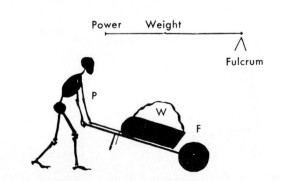

139

Third-class levers

A third-class lever (Fig. 11-3) is designed to produce speed and range of motion movements. Most of the levers in the human body are of this type, which requires a great deal of force to move even a small resistance. A screen door operated by a short spring is an example.

The biceps brachii is a typical example in the body. The biceps brachii, inserting on the bicipital tuberosity of the radius, applies force between the axis (the elbow joint) and the resistance (the center of gravity of the forearm).

The brachialis is an example of true third-class leverage. It pulls on the ulna just below the elbow, and, since the ulna cannot rotate, the pull is direct and true. The biceps brachii, on the other hand, supinates the forearm as it flexes, so that the third-class leverage applies to flexion only.

Factors in use of anatomical levers

Our anatomical leverage system can be used to gain a mechanical advantage that will improve simple or complex physical movements. Some individuals unconsciously develop habits of making good use of human levers, but frequently this is not true.

Length of lever arms

The distance of the muscle insertion from the joint is important, since the longer the force arm (distance between the joint and muscle insertion), the less force is required to move the lever. Even slight variations in the location of the force and resistance are important in determining the effective force of the muscle.

This point can be illustrated in the following simple formula, using the biceps brachii muscle as a typical example.

$$
\begin{array}{ccccc}
F & \times & FA & = & R & \times & RA \\
\text{(Force)} & & \text{(Force} & & \text{(Resistance)} & & \text{(Resistance} \\
& & \text{arm)} & & & & \text{arm)}
\end{array}
$$

$$2 \text{ inches} = 10 \text{ pounds} \times 9 \text{ inches}$$
$$2\,F = 90 \text{ pounds}$$
$$F = 45 \text{ pounds}$$

Change the insertion 1 inch:

$$3 \text{ inches} = 10 \text{ pounds} \times 9 \text{ inches}$$
$$3\,F = 90 \text{ pounds}$$
$$F = 30 \text{ pounds}$$

Thus a change of 1 inch in the insertion can make a considerable difference in the force necessary to move the lever.

The system of leverage in the human body is built for speed and range of movement at the expense of force. Short force arms and long resistance arms require great muscular strength to produce movement. In the forearm, the attachments of the biceps and triceps muscles clearly illustrate this point, since the force arm of the biceps is 1 to 2 inches and the triceps less than 1 inch. Many other similar examples are found all over the body. From a practical point of view this means that the muscular system should be strong to supply the necessary force for body movements, especially in strenuous sports activities.

FIG. 11-3 • Third-class lever.

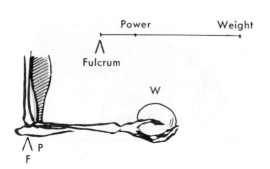

When we speak of human leverage in relation to sport skills, we are generally referring to several levers. For example, in throwing a ball there is a lever at the shoulder, elbow, and wrist joints. In fact, it can be said that there is one long lever from the feet to the hand.

The longer the lever, the more effective it is in imparting velocity. A tennis player can hit a tennis ball harder with a straight-arm drive than with a bent elbow because the lever (including the racket) is longer and moves at a faster speed.

Fig. 11-4 indicates that a longer lever (Z') travels faster than a shorter lever (S') in traveling the same number of degrees. In sports activities in which it is possible to increase the length of a lever with a racket or bat, the same principle applies.

In baseball, hockey, golf, field hockey, and other sports, long levers similarly produce more linear force and thus better performance. For quickness of movement, it is sometimes desirable to have a short lever arm, such as when a baseball catcher brings his hand back to his ear to secure a quick throw or when a sprinter shortens his knee lever through flexion so much that he almost catches his spikes in his gluteal muscles.

FIG. 11-4 • Length of levers.

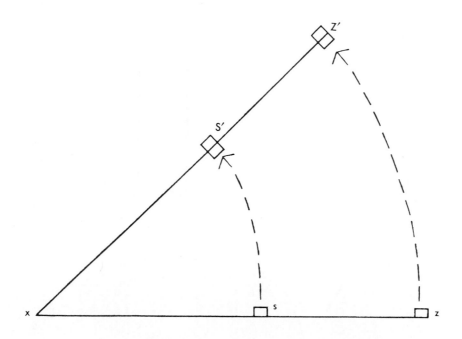

Angle of pull

Another factor of considerable importance in using the leverage system is the angle of pull of the muscles on the bone. Joint movements and insertion angles involve mostly small angles of pull. The angle increases as the bone moves away from its anatomical position through the contraction of the local muscle group. This range of movement depends on the type of joint and bony structure.

Most muscles work at a small angle of pull, generally less than 50 degrees. At 90 degrees, all of the force of a muscle is turning force. At all other degrees of an angle, there are two components of force—one turning force, A, and the other stabilizing force, B—through the joint or a dislocating force, when the movement has gone beyond 90 degrees (Fig. 11-5).

It is desirable in some activities to have a person begin a movement when the joint angle is at 90 degrees. Many boys and girls are unable to do a chin (pull-up) unless they start at a 90-degree angle at the elbow joint, since it is easier because of the more advantageous angle of pull. The application of this fact can compensate for lack of sufficient strength. In its range of motion, a muscle pulls a lever through a range characteristic of itself, but in approaching and going beyond 90 degrees, it is most effective. An increase in strength is the only solution for those muscles which operate at disadvantageous angles of pull and require a greater force to operate efficiently.

FIG. 11-5 • Components of force.

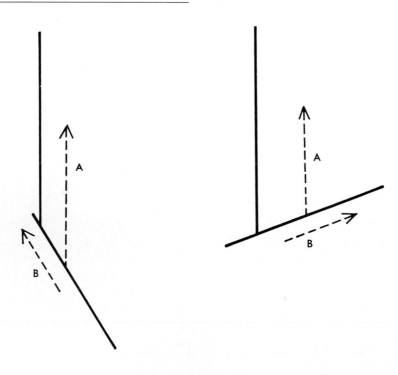

Laws of motion and physical activities

Motion is fundamental in physical education and sports activity. Body motion is generally produced or at least started by some action of the muscular system. No motion can occur without a force, and the muscular system is the source of force in the human body. Thus development of the muscular system is indispensable to movement.

Basically, there are two types of motion: *linear motion* (motion in a straight line) and *angular motion* (motion around an axis, which in the human body is provided by the various joints). In a sense, these two types of motion are related, since angular motion of the joints can produce the linear motion of walking. For example, in many sports activities the cumulative angular motion of the joints of the body imparts linear motion to a thrown object (ball, shot) or to an object struck with an instrument (bat, racket).

A brief review of Newton's laws of motion will indicate the many applications of these laws to physical education activities and sports. Newton's laws explain all the characteristics of motion and are fundamental to understanding human movement.

Law of inertia

A body in motion tends to remain in motion at the same speed in a straight line; a body at rest tends to remain at rest unless acted on by a force.

Muscles produce the force necessary to start motion, stop motion, accelerate motion, decelerate motion, or change the direction of motion. Put another way, inertia is the reluctance to change status; only force can do it.

Numerous examples of this law are found in physical education activities. A sprinter in his starting blocks has to apply considerable force to overcome his resting inertia. A runner on an indoor track has to apply considerable force to overcome moving inertia and stop before hitting the wall. Balls and other objects that are thrown or struck require force to stop them. Starting, stopping, and changing direction—a part of many physical activities—provide many other examples of the law of inertia applied to body motion.

Since force is required to change inertia, it is obvious that any activity that is carried out at a steady pace in a consistent direction will conserve energy, and any irregularly paced or directed activity will be very costly to energy reserves. This explains in part why activities such as handball and basketball are so much more fatiguing than jogging or dancing.

Law of acceleration

A change in the acceleration of a body is directly proportional to the force causing it and inversely proportional to the mass of the body.

To attain speed in moving the body, a strong muscular force is generally necessary. Weight, or more technically "mass" $\left(\dfrac{\text{weight}}{\text{gravity}} \right)$, affects the speed and acceleration in physical movements. It requires a much greater force from the muscles to accelerate a 230-pound man than it does a 130-pound man to the same running speed. Also, it is possible to accelerate a baseball faster than a shot because of the difference in weight. The force required to run at half speed is less than the force required to run at top speed. To impart speed to a ball or an object, it is necessary to accelerate rapidly the part of the body holding the object.

Football, basketball, track, and field hockey are a few sports that demand speed and acceleration.

Law of reaction

For every action there is an opposite and equal reaction.

A supporting surface provides resistance force equal to the force that we place on it as we walk or run over it. It is easier to run on a hard track than on a sandy beach because of the difference in the reactions of the two surfaces. The track resists the runner's propulsion force, and the reaction drives the runner ahead. The sand dissipates the runner's force, and the reaction force is correspondingly reduced with the apparent loss in forward force and speed. A sprinter applies a force in excess of 300 pounds on his starting blocks, which resist with an equal force. When a body is in flight, as it is in jumping, movement of one part of the body produces a reaction in another part. This occurs because there is no resistive surface to supply a reaction force.

Balance or equilibrium

Balance is important for the resting body as well as for the moving body. Generally, balance is to be desired, but there are circumstances in which movement is improved when the body tends to be unbalanced. Following are certain general factors that apply to balance:

1. A person has balance when the center of gravity falls within the base.
2. A person has balance in the direct proportion to the size of the base. The larger the base, the more balance.
3. A person has balance in proportion to the weight (mass). The greater the weight, the more balance.
4. A person has balance depending on the height of the center of gravity. The lower the center of gravity, the more balance.
5. A person has balance depending on where the center of gravity is in the base of support. The balance is less if the center of gravity is near the edge of the base.
6. Rotation about an axis aids balance. A moving bike is easier to balance than a stationary bike.
7. Kinesthetic physiological functions contribute to balance. The semicircular canals of the inner ear, vision, touch (pressure), and kinesthetic sense all provide balance information to the performer.

Balance—or equilibrium, as it is frequently called—is essential in all movements. It is affected by the constant force of gravity.

Walking has been described as an activity in which a person throws the body in and out of balance with each step. In rapid running movements the individual has to lower the center of gravity to maintain balance when stopping or changing direction. Jumping activities, on the other hand, attempt to raise the center of gravity as high as possible.

Force

Muscles are the main source of force that produces or changes movement of a body segment, the entire body, or some object thrown, struck, or stopped. Strong muscles are able to produce more force than weak muscles. This refers to both maximum and sustained exertion over a period of time.

Force is defined as mass times acceleration. For our purposes the weight is the mass. The weight of a body segment or the entire body times the speed of acceleration determines the force.

Obviously in football this is very important. Yet it is just as important in other activities that use only a part of the human body. When one throws a ball, the force applied to the ball is equal to the weight of the arm times the speed of acceleration of the arm. Also, as previously discussed, the leverage factor is important.

The quantity of motion or, more scientifically stated, the *momentum*, which is equal to mass times velocity, is important in skill activities. It is not necessary to apply maximum force and thus increase the momentum of a ball or object being struck in all situations. In skillful performance, regulation of the amount of force is necessary. Judgment as to the amount of force required to throw a softball a given distance, hit a golf ball 200 yards, or hit a tennis ball across the net and into the court is important.

In activities involving movement of various joints, as in throwing a ball or putting a shot, there should be a summation of forces from the beginning of movement in the lower segment of the body to the twisting of the trunk and movement at the shoulder, elbow, and wrist joints. The speed at which a golf club strikes the ball is the result of a summation of forces of the trunk, shoulders, arms, and wrists. Shot-putting and discus and javelin throwing are other good examples to show that summation of forces is essential.

Throwing

In the performance of various sport skills, many applications of the laws of leverage, motion, and balance may be found. A skill common to many activities is throwing. The object thrown may be some type of ball, but it is frequently an object of another size or shape, such as a rock, beanbag, Frisbee, discus, or javelin.

A brief analysis of some of the basic mechanical principles involved in the skill of throwing will help to indicate the importance of understanding the applications of these principles. Many activities involve these and sometimes other mechanical principles.

Motion is basic to throwing when the angular motion (p. 143) of the levers (bones) of the body (trunk, shoulder, elbow, and wrist) is used to give linear motion to the ball when it is released.

Newton's laws of motion apply in throwing because the individual's inertia and the ball's inertia (p. 143) must be overcome by the application of force. The muscles of the body provide the force to move the body parts and the ball held in the hand. The *law of acceleration* (Newton's second law) comes into operation with the muscular force that is necessary to accelerate the arm, wrist, and hand. The greater the force (mass times acceleration) that a person can produce, the faster the arm will move, and thus the greater the speed that will be imparted to the ball. The reaction of the feet against the surface on which the subject stands indicates the application of the *law of reaction*.

The leverage factor is very important in throwing a ball or object. The longer the lever, the greater is the speed that can be imparted to the ball. For all practical purposes, the body from the feet to the fingers can be considered as one long lever. The longer the lever, either from natural body length or from the movements of the body to the extended backward position (as in throwing a softball, with extension of the shoulder and the elbow joints), the greater will be the arc through which it accelerates and thus the greater the speed imparted to the thrown object.

In certain circumstances, when the ball is to be thrown only a short distance, as in baseball when it is thrown by the catcher to the bases, the short lever would be advantageous because it is faster. Balance or equilibrium is a factor in throwing when the body is rotated to the rear in the beginning of the throw. This motion moves the body nearly out of balance to the rear, and then balance changes again in the body with the forward movement. Balance is again established with the follow-through when the feet are spread and the knees and trunk are flexed to lower the center of gravity.

Summary

The preceding discussion has been a brief overview of some of the factors affecting motion. Analysis of human motion in light of the laws of physics poses a problem: how comprehensive is the analysis to be? This analysis can become very complex, particularly when body motion is combined with the manipulation of an object in the hand involved in the throwing, kicking, striking, or catching.

These factors become involved when an analysis is attempted of the activities common to our physical education program—football, baseball, basketball, track and field, field hockey, and swimming, to mention a few. However, a physical educator who is to have a complete view of which factors control human movement must have a working knowledge of both the physiological and the biomechanical principles of kinesiology.

It is beyond the scope of this book to make a detailed analysis of other activities. If this information is desired, a number of good sources that consider these problems in detail are given in the Selected References.

Laboratory and review exercises

1 Special projects and class reports by individual or small groups of students on the mechanical analysis of all the skills involved in the following:
   a. Basketball
   b. Baseball
   c. Dancing
   d. Diving
   e. Football
   f. Field Hockey
   g. Golf
   h. Gymnastics
   i. Soccer
   j. Swimming
   k. Tennis
   l. Wrestling

2 Term projects and special class reports by individual or small groups of students about the following factors in motion:
   a. Balance or equilibrium
   b. Force
   c. Gravity
   d. Motion
   e. Leverage
   f. Projectiles
   g. Friction
   h. Buoyancy
   i. Aerodynamics
   j. Hydrodynamics
   k. Restitution
   l. Spin
   m. Rebound angle
   n. Momentum

3 Demonstrations, term projects, or special reports by individual or small groups of students on the following activities:
   a. Lifting
   b. Throwing and catching
   c. Standing
   d. Walking
   e. Running
   f. Jumping
   g. Falling
   h. Sitting
   i. Pushing and pulling
   j. Striking

Selected references

Barham JN: Mechanical kinesiology, St. Louis, 1978, The CV Mosby Co.

Broer MR: An introduction to kinesiology, Englewood Cliffs, NJ, 1968, Prentice-Hall, Inc.

Broer MR, and Zernicke RF: Efficiency of human movement, ed. 3, Philadelphia, 1979, WB Saunders Co.

Bunn JW: Scientific principles of coaching, ed. 2, Englewood Cliffs, NJ, 1972, Prentice-Hall, Inc.

Cooper JM, Adrian M and Glassow RB: Kinesiology, ed. 5, St. Louis, 1982, The CV Mosby Co.

Exer-Genie instruction manual, Fullerton, Calif., 1966, Exer-Genie, Inc.

Hinson M: Kinesiology, ed. 2, Dubuque, Ia., 1981, William C. Brown Group.

Kelley DL: Kinesiology: fundamentals of motion description, Englewood Cliffs, NJ, 1971, Prentice-Hall, Inc.

Logan GA and McKinney WC: Anatomic kinesiology, ed. 3, Dubuque, Ia., 1982, William C. Brown Group.

Piscopo J and Baley J: Kinesiology: the science of movement, New York, 1981, John Wiley & Sons, Inc.

Rasch PJ and Burke RK: Kinesiology and applied anatomy, ed. 6, Philadelphia, 1978, Lea & Febiger.

*Royal Canadian Air Force exercise plans for physical fitness; XBX-Women, 5BX-Men, Mt. Vernon, N.Y., 1962.

Scott MG: Analysis of human motion, ed. 2, New York, 1963, Appleton-Century-Crofts.

Wells KF and Luttgens K: Kinesiology, ed. 7, Philadelphia, 1982, WB Saunders Co.

---

*Information on conditioning exercises.

Glossary

abduction Movement away from the axis or trunk, as in raising the arms to the side horizontally, leg sideward, and scapula away from the spinal column.

adduction Movement toward the axis or trunk, as in lowering the arm to the side or the leg to the anatomical position.

agonist A muscle or muscle group that produces a designated movement by contraction.

amphiarthrosis Movement of joints brought about by the compression of discs, as in the spinal column (vertebra on vertebra).

anatomical position The subject is in the standing position, with feet together and palms of hands facing forward.

antagonist A muscle or muscle group that counteracts the contraction of another muscle or muscle group.

arthrodial joints Joints in which bones glide on each other in limited movement, as in the bones of the wrist (carpal) or bones of the foot (tarsal).

ball-and-socket joints Joints that permit movement in all planes and rotation, as in the shoulder or hip joints.

circumduction Circular movement of a bone at the joint, as in movement of the hip, shoulder, or trunk around a fixed point.

concentric contraction A contraction in which there is a shortening of the muscle.

condyloid joint Movement of a joint in two planes, backward and forward or side to side, as in movement of the radium and ulna on the carpal bones.

distal Farthest from the midline or point of reference; the hand is the distal part of the shoulder area.

eccentric contraction Lengthening of a muscle as a result of the force of gravity or a greater force than the contractile force.

eversion Turning the sole of the foot outward with weight on the inside of the foot.

extension Movement of the bones apart or straightening a joint, as in the elbow or knee joint.

first-class lever A lever in which the axis (fulcrum) is between the force and the resistance, as in the extension of the elbow joint.

flexion Movement of the bones toward each other at a joint by decreasing the angle, as at the elbow or knee joints.

hamstrings A common name given to the group of posterior thigh muscles: biceps femoris, semitendinous, and semimembranosus.

insertion The most movable attachment of a muscle, generally the farthest from the midline.

intrinsic muscles Small, deep muscles found in the foot and hand.

inversion Turning of the sole inward with weight on the outer edge of the foot.

isometric contraction A type of contraction with little or no shortening of the muscle when the resistance cannot be overcome.

kinesiology The science of movement, which includes anatomical (structural) and biomechanical (mechanical) aspects of movement.

lever A rigid bar (bone) that moves about an axis.

ligament A type of tough connective tissue that attaches bone to bone.

origin The less movable attachment of a muscle, generally closest to the midline of the body.

plantar flexion Movement of the sole (underpart) of the foot downward.

pronation Rotation on the axis of a bone as in turning the hand palm-down by rotating the radius on the ulna.

proximal Nearest to the midline or point of reference, the first digit of the hand or foot is proximal to the metatarsal.

quadriceps A common name given to the four muscles of the anterior aspect of the thigh: rectus femoris, vastus medialis, vastus intermedius, and vastus lateralis.

rotation Movement around an axis, such as the turning inward, outward, downward, or upward of a bone.

supination Rotation on the axis of bone, as in turning the hand palm-up by the rotation of the radius on the ulna.

third-class lever A lever where the force (effort) is between the axis (fulcrum) and the resistance, as in flexion of the elbow joint.

Index

Page numbers in italics indicate illustration only.

149

Worksheets

CHAPTER ONE
Worksheet No. 1
On the posterior skeletal worksheet list the names of the bones and
all of the prominent features of each bone.

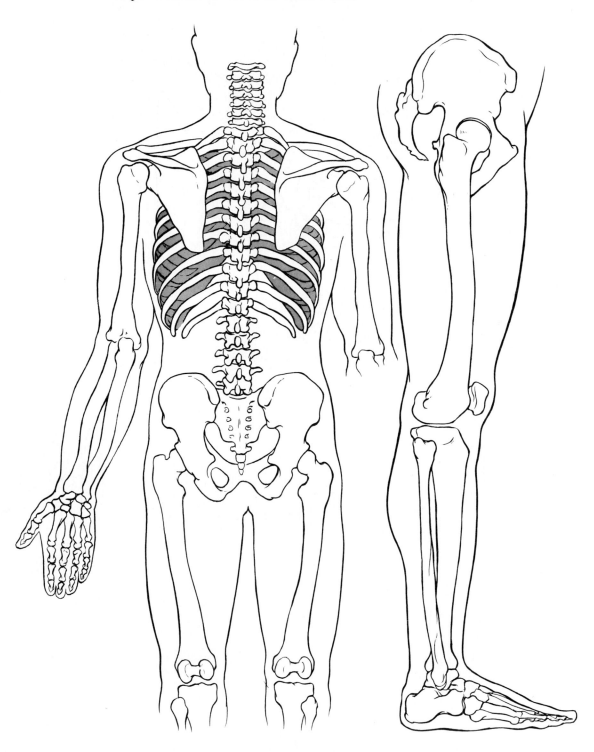

Worksheet No. 2
On the anterior skeletal worksheet list the names of the bones and
all of the prominent features of each bone.

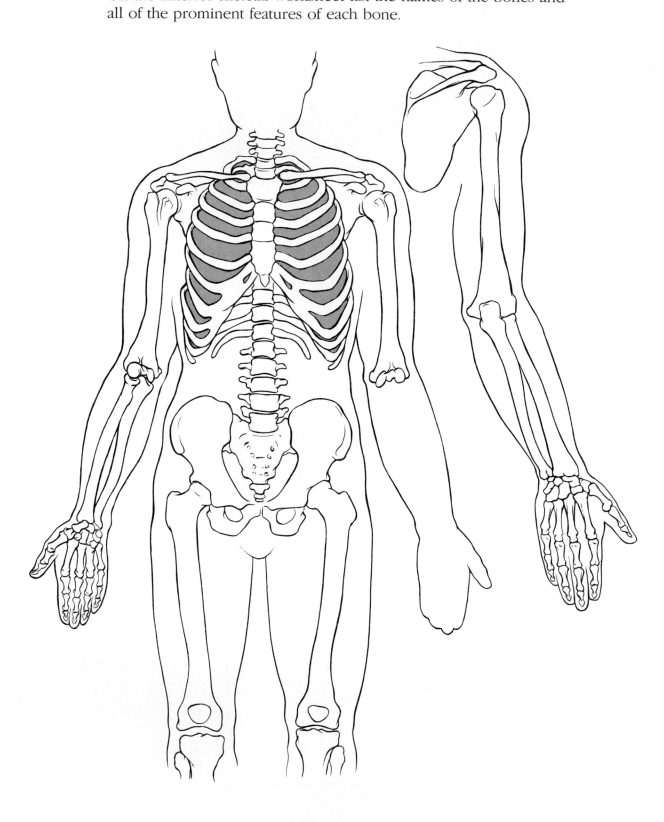

CHAPTER TWO
Worksheet No. 1
Draw and label on the worksheet the following listed muscles
a. Trapezius
b. Rhomboideus major and minor
c. Serratus anterior
d. Levator scapulae

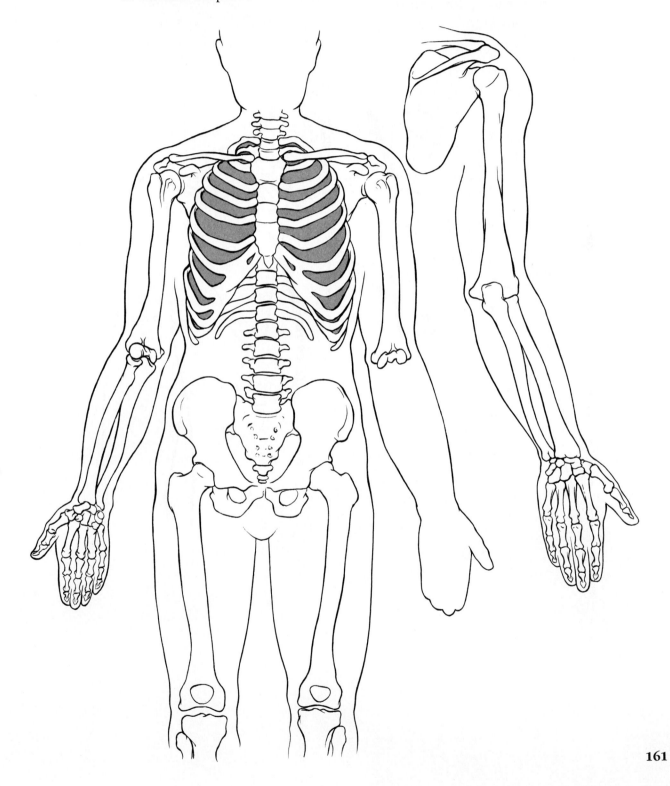

CHAPTER TWO
Worksheet No. 2
Label and indicate by arrows the following movements of the
shoulder girdle.
a. Adduction
b. Abduction
c. Rotation upward
d. Rotation downward
e. Elevation
f. Depression

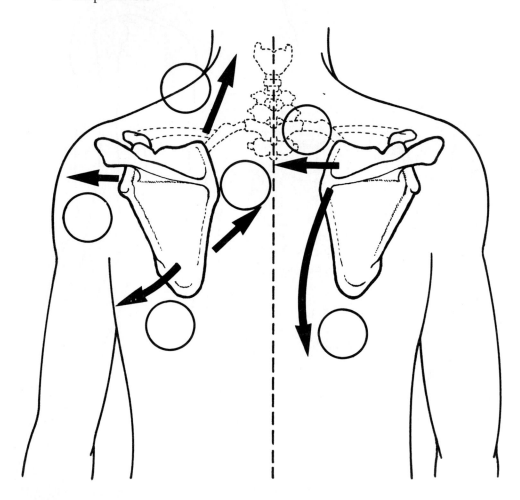

CHAPTER THREE
Worksheet No. 1
Draw and label on the worksheet the following muscles:

a. Deltoideus
b. Supraspinatus
c. Subscapularis
d. Teres major

e. Infraspinatus and teres minor
f. Latissimus dorsi
g. Pectoralis major

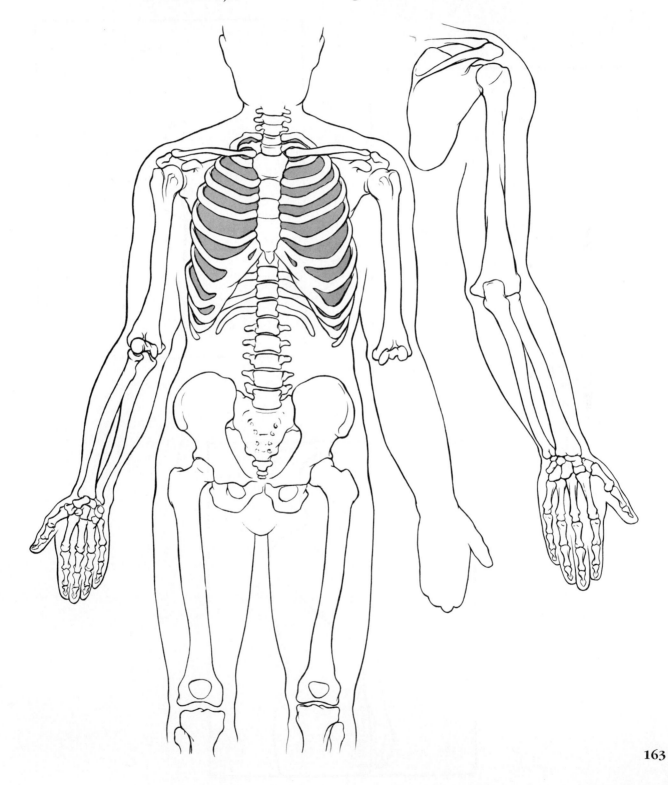

CHAPTER THREE
Worksheet No. 2
Label and indicate by arrows the following listed movements of the shoulder joint:

a. Abduction
b. Adduction
c. Flexion

d. Extension
e. Horizontal flexion (adduction)
f. Horizontal extension (extension)

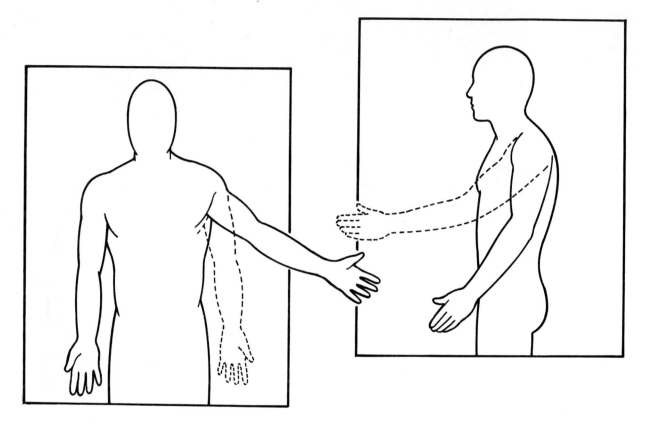

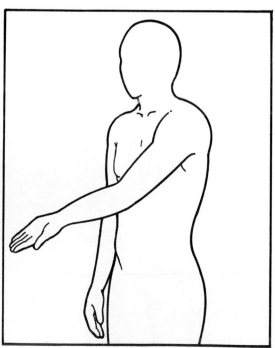

CHAPTER FOUR
Worksheet No. 1
Draw and label on the worksheet the following muscles.
a. Biceps brachii   e. Supinator
b. Brachioradialis   f. Triceps brachii
c. Brachialis   g. Anconeus
d. Pronator teres

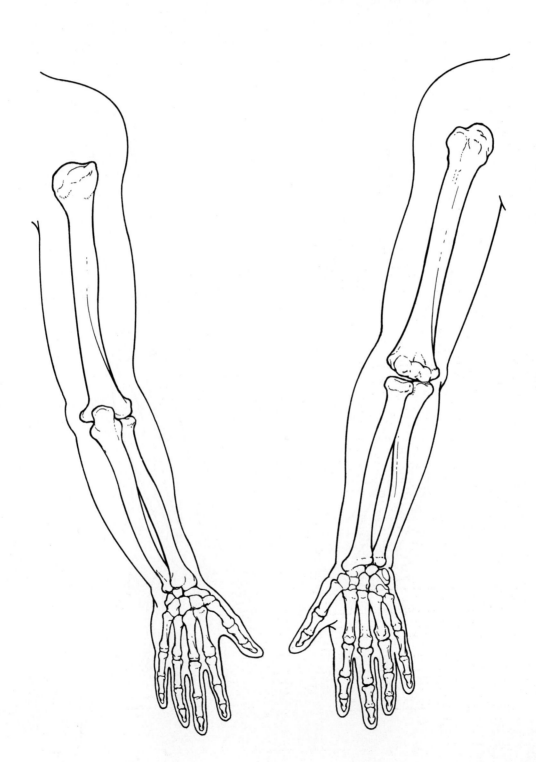

CHAPTER FOUR
Worksheet No. 2
Draw and label on the worksheet the following muscles.
a. Flexor pollicis longus
b. Flexor carpi radialis
c. Flexor carpi ulnaris
d. Extensor digitorum communis
e. Extensor pollicis longus
f. Extensor carpi ulnaris

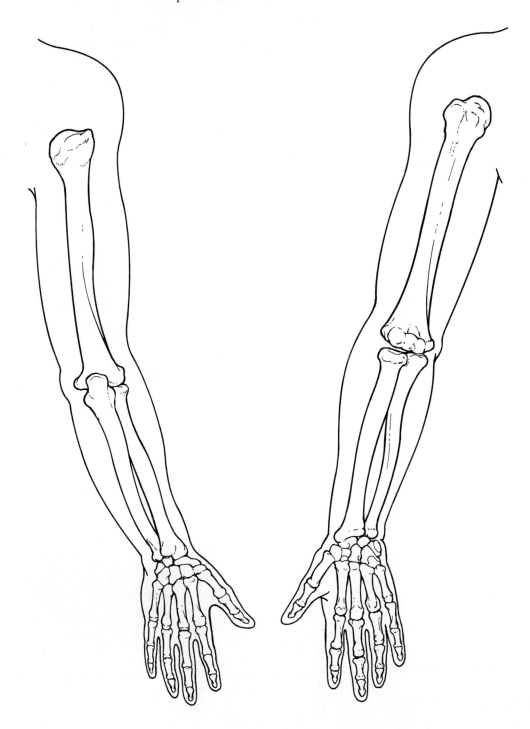

CHAPTER FOUR
Worksheet No. 3
Label and indicate by arrows the following movements of the elbow
joint and wrist and hands.

Elbow joint	Wrist and hands
Flexion	Flexion
Extension	Extension
Pronation	
Supination	

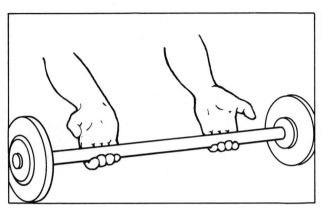

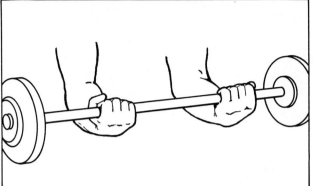

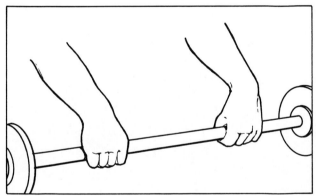

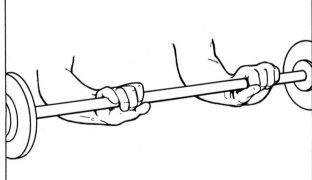

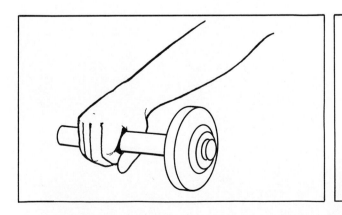

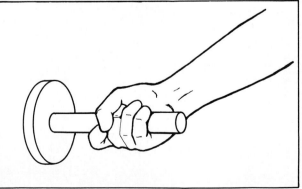

CHAPTER FIVE
Worksheet No. 1
Analyze this exercise following the procedures explained in this chapter that include joint movements and muscles that produce these movements.

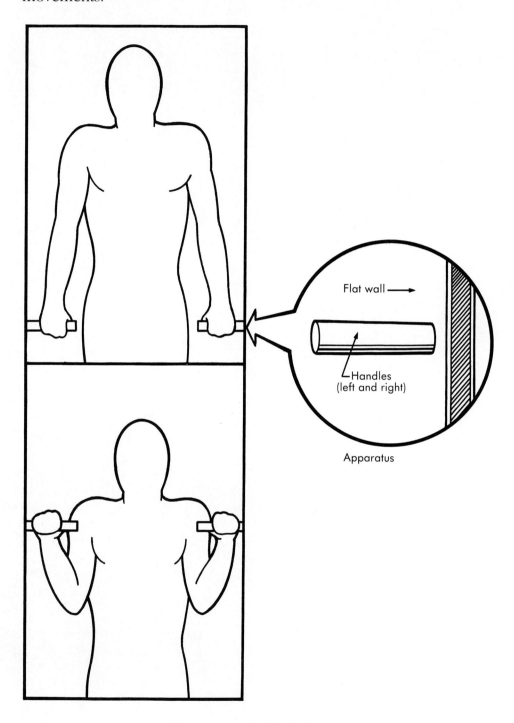

Flat wall →

Handles
(left and right)

Apparatus

CHAPTER SIX
Worksheet No. 1
Draw and label on the worksheet the anterior hip joint and pelvic
girdle muscles.

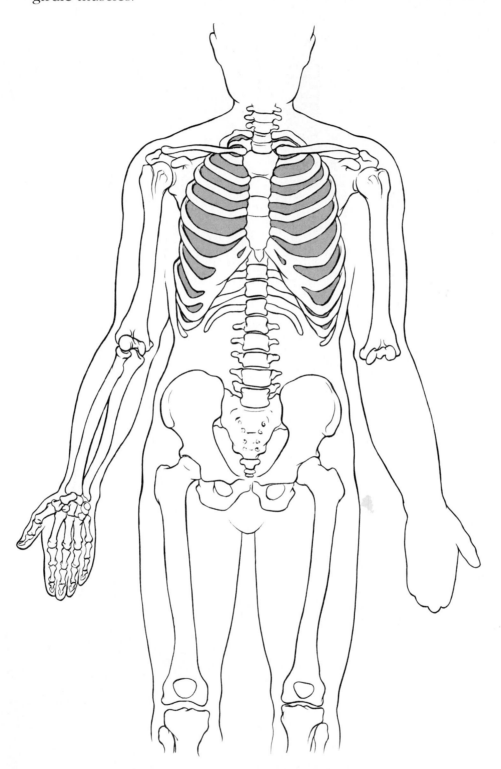

CHAPTER SIX
Worksheet No. 2
Draw and label on the worksheet the posterior hip and pelvic girdle
muscles.

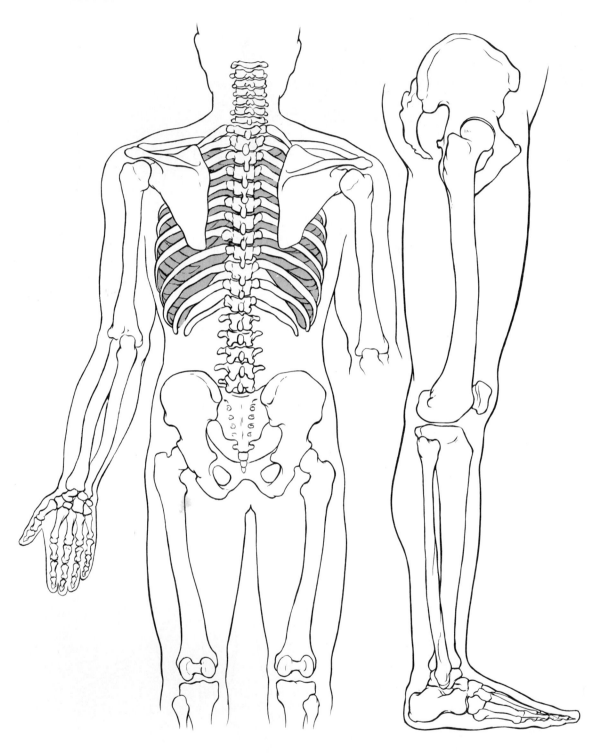

CHAPTER SEVEN
Worksheet No. 1
Draw and label on the worksheet the knee joint muscles.

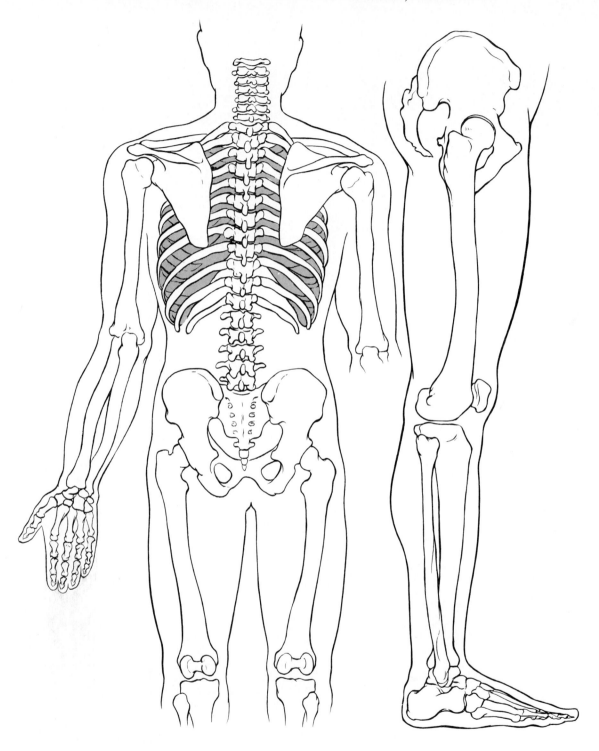

CHAPTER EIGHT
Worksheet No. 1
Draw and label on the worksheet the following muscles of the ankle
and foot.

a. Tibialis anterior
b. Extensor digitorum longus
c. Peroneus longus
d. Peroneus brevis
e. Soleus

f. Gastrocnemius
g. Extensor hallucis longus
h. Tibialis posterior
i. Flexor digitorum longus
j. Flexor hallucis longus

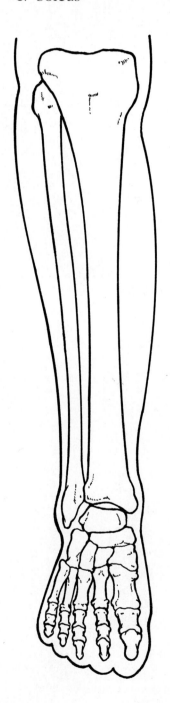
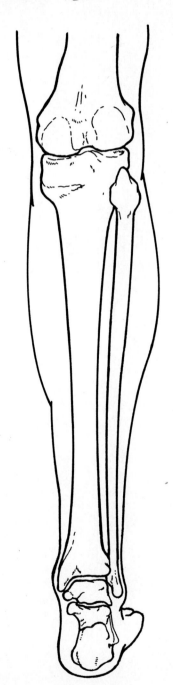

CHAPTER NINE
Worksheet No. 1
Draw and label the following muscles on the skeletal chart.
a. Rectus adbominis
b. Oblique externus abdominis
c. Obliquus internus abdominis

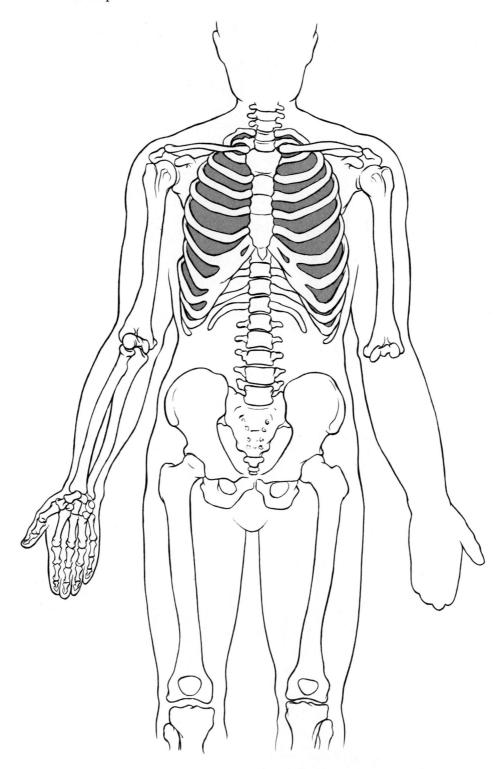

CHAPTER NINE
Worksheet No. 2
Draw and label the following muscles on the skeletal chart.
a. Erector spinae
b. Quadratus lumborum
c. Splenius- cervicis and capitis

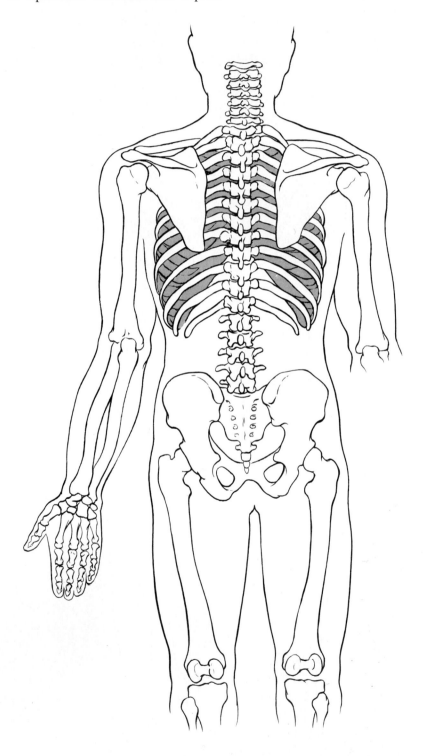